Let's Get Ready For
FIRST GRADE

W9-CNB-790

**Download the 20 songs for FREE
from www.twinsisters.com.**
Go to page 2 for the promo code.

Learning with music is EASY & FUN!

1. The Consonant Song
2. Learning Our Short Vowels
3. Learning Our Long Vowels
4. The Silent "e"
5. Q And U Are Friends
6. Blends Are Consonant Friends
7. Letters "c" and "g" Have Two Sounds
8. Rhyming Word Rule
9. A Little Cat, Cat, Cat
10. Two Letters Are Hanging Around

11. The Diphthong Song
12. The Antonym Naming Game
13. Similar Synonyms
14. It's A Home Run
15. The Island Of Learning
16. The Two-More-Than Strategy
17. I'm Jumpin' To The Beat Of The Music
18. There's No Doubt About It
19. The Answer Stays The Same
20. Just Count Down One

Songs Written By: **Kim Mitzo Thompson, Karen Mitzo Hilderbrand**
Executive Producers: **Kim Mitzo Thompson, Karen Mitzo Hilderbrand**
Music Arranged By: **Hal Wright**
Music Vocals: **Nashville Kids Sound**

DEAR PARENTS & TEACHERS,

Written as a resource to help children build a foundation of learning skills that will align with the Common Core State Standards for First Grade, this workbook provides a variety of engaging English-Language Arts and Mathematics activities.

What Are Common Core State Standards?
According to CoreStandards.org,

"The Common Core State Standards Initiative is a state-led effort coordinated by the National Governors Association Center for Best Practices (NGA Center) and the Council of Chief State School Officers (CCSSO). The standards were developed in collaboration with teachers, school administrators, and experts, to provide a clear and consistent framework to prepare our children for college and the workforce."

In order for teachers and parents to establish appropriate benchmarks for students, the Common Core State Standards help communicate what is expected at each grade level. The standards included in this workbook are conveniently listed on page 4-5 for ease in creating lesson plans reinforcing the skills that support CCSS.

Children learn in a variety of ways. Using music makes learning basic skills fun and engages children in the learning process. Download the 20 FREE songs and use in conjunction with this workbook.

Let's work together to ensure all children are well prepared for the future and are given the tools they need for success!

Sincerely,

Kim Mitzo Thompson,
MS Elementary Education

Download the 20 songs for **FREE** from
www.twinsisters.com
Enter Promo Code: **BN1GRA**

Language Table of Contents:

Math Table of Contents:

Reading And Language Arts

English Language Arts Standards > Reading: Informational Text > Grade 1

Key Ideas and Details

CCSS.ELA-Literacy.RI.1.1 Ask and answer questions about key details in a text.

CCSS.ELA-Literacy.RI.1.2 Win topic and retell key details of a text.

CCSS.ELA-Literacy.RI.1.3 Describe the connection between two individuals, events, ideas, or pieces of information in a text.

Craft and Structure

CCSS.ELA-Literacy.RI.1.6 Distinguish between information provided by pictures or other illustrations and information provided by the words in a text.

Integration of Knowledge and Ideas

CCSS.ELA-Literacy.RI.1.7 Use the illustrations and details in a text to describe its key ideas.

Range of Reading and Level of Text Complexity

CCSS.ELA-Literacy.RI.1.10 With prompting and support, read informational texts appropriately complex for grade 1.

English Language Arts Standards > Reading: Foundational Skills > Grade 1

Print Concepts

CCSS.ELA-Literacy.RF.1.1 Demonstrate understanding of the organization and basic features of print.

CCSS.ELA-Literacy.RF.1.1a Recognize the distinguishing features of a sentence (e.g., first word, capitalization, ending punctuation).

Phonological Awareness

CCSS.ELA-Literacy.RF.1.2 Demonstrate understanding of spoken words, syllables, and sounds (phonemes).

CCSS.ELA-Literacy.RF.1.2a Distinguish long from short vowel sounds in spoken single-syllable words.

CCSS.ELA-Literacy.RF.1.2b Orally produce single-syllable words by blending sounds (phonemes), including consonant blends.

CCSS.ELA-Literacy.RF.1.2c Isolate and pronounce initial, medial vowel, and final sounds (phonemes) in spoken single-syllable words.

CCSS.ELA-Literacy.RF.1.2d Segment spoken single-syllable words into their complete sequence of individual sounds (phonemes).

Phonics and Word Recognition

CCSS.ELA-Literacy.RF.1.3 Know and apply grade-level phonics and word analysis skills in decoding words.

CCSS.ELA-Literacy.RF.1.3a Know the spelling-sound correspondences for common consonant digraphs.

CCSS.ELA-Literacy.RF.1.3b Decode regularly spelled one-syllable words.

CCSS.ELA-Literacy.RF.1.3c Know final –e and common vowel team conventions for representing long vowel sounds

CCSS.ELA-Literacy.RF.1.3f Read words with inflectional endings.

CCSS.ELA-Literacy.RF.1.3g Recognize and read grade-appropriate irregularly spelled words.

Fluency

CCSS.ELA-Literacy.RF.1.4 Read with sufficient accuracy and fluency to support comprehension.

CCSS.ELA-Literacy.RF.1.4a Read grade-level text with purpose and understanding.

CCSS.ELA-Literacy.RF.1.4b Read grade-level text orally with accuracy, appropriate rate, and expression on successive readings.

CCSS.ELA-Literacy.RF.1.4c Use context to confirm or self-correct word recognition and understanding, rereading as necessary.

English Language Arts Standards > Language > Grade 1

Conventions of Standard English

    CCSS.ELA-Literacy.L.1.1 Demonstrate command of the conventions of standard English grammar and usage when writing or speaking.

    CCSS.ELA-Literacy.L.1.1b Use common, proper, and possessive nouns.

    CCSS.ELA-Literacy.L.1.1c Use singular and plural nouns with matching verbs in basic sentences (e.g. He hops; We hop).

    CCSS.ELA-Literacy.L.1.1d Use personal, possessive, and indefinite pronouns (e.g., I, me, my, they, them, their, anyone, everything).

    CCSS.ELA-Literacy.L.1.1e Use verbs to convey a sense of past, present and future (e.g., Yesterday I walked home; Today I walk home; Tomorrow I will walk home).

    CCSS.ELA-Literacy.L.1.1f Use frequently occurring adjectives.

    CCSS.ELA-Literacy.L.1.1j Produce and expand complete simple and compound declarative, interrogative, imperative, and exclamatory sentences in response to prompts.

    CCSS.ELA-Literacy.L.1.2 Demonstrate command of the conventions of standard English capitalization, punctuation, and spelling when writing.

    CCSS.ELA-Literacy.L.1.2a Capitalize dates and names of people.

    CCSS.ELA-Literacy.L.1.2b Use end punctuation for sentences.

    CCSS.ELA-Literacy.L.1.2e Spell untaught words phonetically, drawing on phonemic awareness and spelling conventions.

Vocabulary Acquisition and Use

    CCSS.ELA-Literacy.L.1.4 Determine or clarify the meaning of unknown and multiple-meaning words and phrases based on grade 1 reading and content, choosing flexibly from an array of strategies.

    CCSS.ELA-Literacy.L.1.4a Use sentence-level context as a clue to the meaning of a word or phrase.

    CCSS.ELA-Literacy.L.1.4c Identify frequently occurring root words (e.g., look) and their inflectional forms (e.g., looks, looked, looking).

Mathematics

Operations and Algebraic Thinking 1.0A

- Represent and solve problems involving addition and subtraction.
- Understand and apply properties of operations and the relationship between addition and subtraction.
- Add and subtract within 20.
- Work with addition and subtraction equations

Number and Operations in Base Ten 1.NBT

- Extend the counting sequence.
- Understand place value.
- Use place value understanding and properties of operations to add and subtract.

Measurement and Data 1.MD

- Measure lengths indirectly and by iterating length units.
- Tell and write time.
- Represent and interpret data.

Geometry 1.G

- Reason with shapes and their attributes.

Name_____ Date _____

The beginning sound in **seal** is spelled
with the letter **s**.

<u>s</u>eal

Say the name of each picture. Circle the pictures in each row that
have the same beginning sound as **seal**.

1.

2.

3.

4.

5.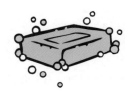

Beginning t

Name_____ Date _____

The beginning sound in **turkey** is spelled with the letter **t**.

turkey

Say the name of each picture. Circle the pictures in each row that have the same beginning sound as **turkey**.

1.

2.

3.

4.

5.

7

Name_____ Date_____

The beginning sound in **bicycle** is spelled with the letter **b**.

bicycle

Name the pictures. Write **b** below each picture that has the same beginning sound as **bicycle**.

1. ___ ___ ___ ___

2. ___ ___ ___ ___

Write **b** to complete each word. Say the word.

3. ___ell

4. ___ird

5. ___oy

6. ___ed

Beginning h

Name _____ Date _____

The beginning sound in **hamburger** is spelled with the letter **h**.

<u>h</u>amburger

Unit 1

Say the name of each picture. Color the pictures in each row that have the same beginning sound as **hamburger**.

1.

2.

3.

4.

5.

Beginning m

Name_____ Date _____

The beginning sound in **mouse** is spelled with the letter **m**.

mouse

Say the name of each picture. Write **m** below each picture that has the same beginning sound as **mouse**.

1. _____

2. _____

3. _____

4. _____

5. _____

6. _____

7. _____

8. _____

9. _____

10. _____

11. _____

12. _____

13. _____

14. _____

15. _____

Name_____ Date _____

The beginning sound in **king** is spelled
with the letter **k**.

king

Unit 1

Say the name of each picture. Write **k** below each picture that has
the same beginning sound as **king**.

1. _____   2. _____   3. _____   4. _____   5. _____

6. _____   7. _____   8. _____   9. _____   10. _____

11. _____   12. _____   13. _____   14. _____   15. _____

Beginning Sound Practice

Name_____ Date _____

Say the name of each picture.
Circle the letter that stands for the beginning sound.

1.	2.	3.	4.
h b	b t	m s	k b
5.	6.	7.	8.
t b	k t	h m	s t
9.	10.	11.	12.
m t	b k	s h	m k
13.	14.	15.	16.
h s	t b	m b	t s

Beginning j

Name_____ Date _____

The beginning sound in **jack-o-lantern** is spelled with the letter **j**.

jack-o-lantern

Say the name of each picture. Circle the pictures in each row that have the same beginning sound as **jack-o-lantern**.

1.

2.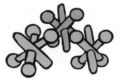

3.

4.

13

Beginning f

Name_____ Date _____

The beginning sound in **fox** is spelled with the letter **f**.

Say the name of each picture. Color the pictures in each row that have the same beginning sound as **fox**.

fox

1.

2.

3.

4.

Beginning g

Name_____ Date _____

The beginning sound in **gift** is spelled with the letter **g**.

Say the name of each picture. Write **g** below each picture that has the same beginning sound as **gift**.

gift

1. _____

2. _____

3. _____

4. _____

5. _____

6. _____

7. _____

8. _____

Look at each picture. Write a word that starts with **g** to finish each rhyme.

_____

a _____ **in a coat**

_____

a **loose** _____

15

Name_____ Date _____

The beginning sound in **lamb** is spelled
with the letter **l**.

lamb

Say the name of each picture. Circle the pictures in
each row that have the same beginning sound as **lamb**.

1.

2.

3.

4.

Beginning d

Name_____ Date_____

The beginning sound in **duck** is spelled
with the letter **d**.

duck

Say the name of each picture. Write **d** below each
picture that has the same beginning sound as **duck**.

1. _ _ _ _ _   2. _ _ _ _ _   3. _ _ _ _ _   4. _ _ _ _ _   5. _ _ _ _ _

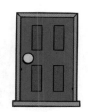    

6. _ _ _ _ _   7. _ _ _ _ _   8. _ _ _ _ _   9. _ _ _ _ _   10. _ _ _ _ _

11. _ _ _ _ _   12. _ _ _ _ _   13. _ _ _ _ _   14. _ _ _ _ _   15. _ _ _ _ _

Unit 1

Name_____ Date_____

The beginning sound in **nest** is spelled with the letter **n**.

nest

Say the name of each picture. Write **n** below each picture that has the same beginning sound as **nest**.

1. _____

2. _____

3. _____

4. _____

5. _____

6. _____

7. _____

8. _____

9. _____

10. _____

11. _____

12. _____

13. _____

14. _____

15. _____

Beginning Sound Practice

Name_____ Date _____

Say the name of each picture. Fill in the circle next to the letter that stands for the sound you hear at the beginning.

1.
- ○ m
- ○ j
- ○ r

2.
- ○ n
- ○ p
- ○ d

3.
- ○ r
- ○ f
- ○ l

4.
- ○ n
- ○ k
- ○ p

5.
- ○ f
- ○ s
- ○ w

6.
- ○ y
- ○ l
- ○ m

7.
- ○ g
- ○ j
- ○ w

8.
- ○ s
- ○ k
- ○ d

9.
- ○ t
- ○ m
- ○ j

10.
- ○ j
- ○ h
- ○ n

11.
- ○ g
- ○ d
- ○ f

12.
- ○ f
- ○ y
- ○ l

Name_____ Date _____

The beginning sound in **witch** is spelled
with the letter **w**.

<u>w</u>itch

Say the name of each picture. Write **w** below each
picture that has the same beginning sound as **witch**.

1. _____

2. _____

3. _____

4. _____

5. _____

6. _____

7. _____

8. _____

Look at each picture. Write a word that starts with **w** to finish each rhyme.

a pig in a _____

a dragon in a _____

Beginning c

Name_____ Date _____

The beginning sound in **cat** is spelled
with the letter **c**.

cat

Say the name of each picture. Circle the pictures in
each row that have the same beginning sound as **cat**.

Unit 1

1.

2.

3.

4.

5.

21

Beginning r

Name_____ Date _____

The beginning sound in **rabbit** is spelled with the letter **r**.

Say the name of each picture. Circle the pictures in each row that have the same beginning sound as **rabbit**.

rabbit

1.

2.

3.

4.

Beginning p

Name_____ Date _____

The beginning sound in **pig** is spelled with the letter **p**.

pig

Say the name of each picture. Circle the pictures in each row that have the same beginning sound as **pig**.

1.

2.

3.

4.

5.

Name_____ Date _____

The beginning sound in **queen** is spelled with the letter **q**.

Say the name of each picture. Write **q** below each picture that has the same beginning sound as **queen**.

queen

1. _____

2. _____

3. _____

4. _____

5. _____

6. _____

7. _____

8. _____

9. _____

10. _____

11. _____

12. _____

Name_____ Date_____

The beginning sound in **violin** is spelled with the letter **v**.

Say the name of each picture. Circle the pictures in each row that have the same beginning sound as **violin**.

<u>v</u>iolin

1.

2.

3.

Write **v** to finish each word.

4.  ____ an   5.  ____ est

6.  ____ alley   7.  ____ ase

Beginning Sound Practice

Name_____ Date _____

Say the name of each picture. Fill in the circle next to the word that names the picture.

1. 	2. 	3. 
○ rig ○ pig	○ pat ○ cat	○ vest ○ pest
4. 	5. 	6. 
○ raccoon ○ caccoon	○ pie ○ vie	○ vuilt ○ quilt
7. 	8. 	9. 
○ can ○ van	○ wug ○ rug	○ vencil ○ pencil
10. 	11. 	12. 
○ volcano ○ wolcano	○ quell ○ well	○ robot ○ wobot

Beginning x, y, and z

Name_____ Date _____

The beginning sound in **x-ray** is spelled with the letter **x**.

The beginning sound in **yak** is spelled with the letter **y**.

The beginning sound in **zoo** is spelled with the letter **z**.

Say the name of each picture. Write **x** below the picture that has the same beginning sound as **x-ray**. Write **y** below the picture that has the same beginning sound as **yak**. Write **z** below the picture that has the same beginning sound as **zoo**.

1. _____

2. _____

3. _____

4. _____

5. _____

6. _____

7. _____

8. _____

9. _____

10. _____

11. _____

12. _____

Ending d and g

The sound at the end of **sad** is spelled with the letter **d**.

The sound at the end of **pig** is spelled with the letter **g**.

Say the name of the first picture in each row.
Circle the other pictures in the row that end with the same sound.

1.

2.

3.

4.

5.

Ending n and t

Name_____ Date _____

The sound at the end of **fan** is spelled with the letter **n**.

The sound at the end of **net** is spelled with the letter **t**.

Say the name of each picture. Fill in the circle next to the letter that stands for the sound you hear at the end.

Unit 1

1. 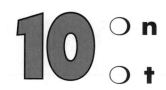 ○ n ○ t	2.  ○ n ○ t	3.  ○ n ○ t	4.  ○ n ○ t
5.  ○ n ○ t	6.  ○ n ○ t	7. 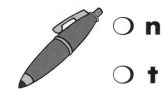 ○ n ○ t	8.  ○ n ○ t
9.  ○ n ○ t	10. ○ n ○ t	11.  ○ n ○ t	12. ○ n ○ t
13.  ○ n ○ t	14.  ○ n ○ t	15.  ○ n ○ t	16.  ○ n ○ t

Ending x and p

The sound at the end of **six** is spelled with the letter **x**.

The sound at the end of **soap** is spelled with the letter **p**.

Say the name of the first picture in each row.
Color the other pictures in the row that end with the same sound.

Ending m and b

Name_____ Date _____

The sound at the end of **drum** is spelled with the letter **m**.

The sound at the end of **sub** is spelled with the letter **b**.

Say the name of the first picture in each row.
Circle the other pictures in the row that end with the same sound.

1.			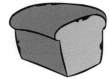	
2.				
3.				
4.				
5.				

Name_____ Date _____

The sound at the end of **yes** 👍 is spelled with the letter **s**.

The sound at the end of **hook** is spelled with the letter **k**.

The sound at the end of **car** 🚗 is spelled with the letter **r**.

Say the name of each picture. Fill in the circle next to the letter that stands for the sound you hear at the end.

1. ○ s ○ k ○ r
2. ○ s ○ k ○ r
3. ○ s ○ k ○ r
4. ○ s ○ k ○ r
5. ○ s ○ k ○ r
6. ○ s ○ k ○ r
7. ○ s ○ k ○ r
8. ○ s ○ k ○ r
9. ○ s ○ k ○ r
10. ○ s ○ k ○ r
11. ○ s ○ k ○ r
12. ○ s ○ k ○ r
13. ○ s ○ k ○ r
14. ○ s ○ k ○ r
15. ○ s ○ k ○ r
16. ○ s ○ k ○ r

Ending Sound Practice

Unit 1

Name_____ Date _____

Say the name of each picture.
Circle the letter that stands for the sound you hear at the end.

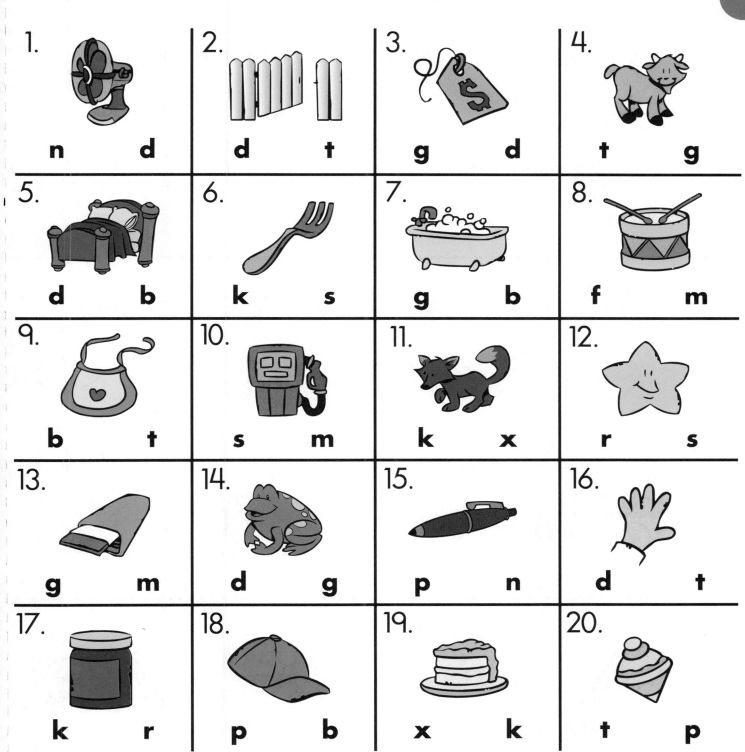

1.   n   d

2.   d   t

3.   g   d

4.   t   g

5.   d   b

6.   k   s

7.   g   b

8.   f   m

9.   b   t

10.   s   m

11.   k   x

12.   r   s

13.   g   m

14.   d   g

15.   p   n

16.   d   t

17.   k   r

18.   p   b

19.   x   k

20.   t   p

Short Vowel a

Name_____ Date _____

The word **hat** has a short **a** sound.

h**a**t

Say the name of each picture.
Color the pictures in each row that have the short **a** sound.

1.

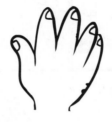

2.

3.

4.

Name_____ Date _____

Say the name of each picture.
Circle the word that names the picture.

1.
cat   cut

2.
cap   cup

3.
hit   hat

4.
can   cin

5.
man   men

6.
tag   tug

7.
mop   map

8.
pan   pin

9.
rim   ram

10.
clom   clam

11.
hand   hund

12.
met   mat

13.
van   ven

14.
rat   rit

15.
fan   fun

16.
jum   jam

17.
bat   bit

18.
bag   bug

19.
him   ham

20.
limp   lamp

Words with -at

Read the words in the box.
Write a word from the box to complete each sentence.

bat	cat	fat	flat	rat	sat

_____

1. The white _____ is sleeping on my lap.

_____

2. A small _____ is eating cheese.

_____

3. Our car has a _____ tire.

_____

4. I _____ on the chair.

_____

5. Tim is up to _____ with two outs.

_____

6. Look at the _____ pig!

Words with -an

Name_____ Date _____

Read the words in the box.
Write a word from the box to complete each sentence.

| **Dan** | **fan** | **man** | **pan** | **ran** | **van** |

_____

- - - - - - - - - - -

1. Jan _____ to catch the bus.
_____

_____

- - - - - - - - - - -

2. We will ride in the green _____ .
_____

_____

- - - - - - - - - - -

3. My brother _____ likes to eat jam.
_____

_____

- - - - - - - - - - -

4. If it is hot, turn on the _____ .
_____

_____

- - - - - - - - - - -

5. Mom put the ham in a _____ .
_____

_____

- - - - - - - - - - -

6. When he grows up he will be a _____ .

Short Vowel i

Name_____ Date _____

The word **pin** has the short **i** sound.

Say the name of each picture.
Circle the pictures in each row that have the short **i** sound.

p<u>i</u>n

1.

2.

3.

4.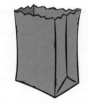

5.

Short Vowel i

Name_____ Date _____

The word **dig** has the short **i** sound.

Say the name of each picture.
Circle the word that names each picture.

d**i**g

Unit 2

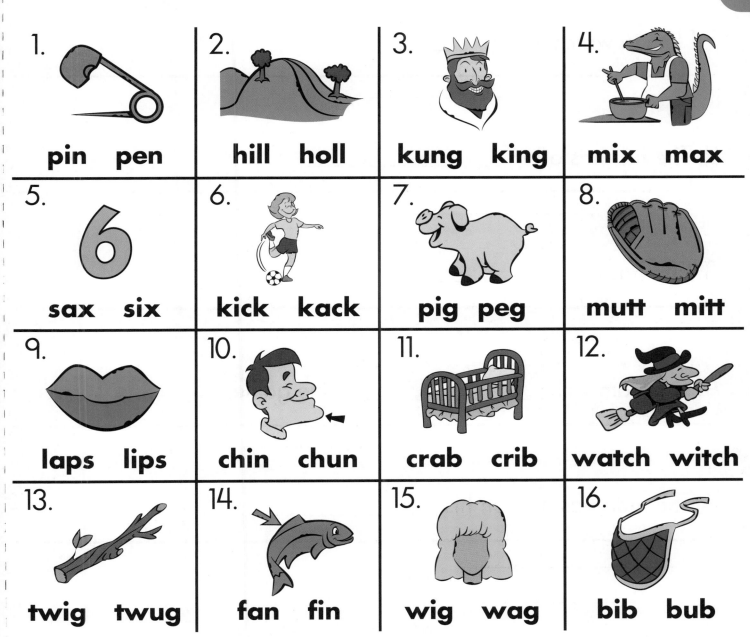

1. pin pen	2. hill holl	3. kung king	4. mix max
5. sax six	6. kick kack	7. pig peg	8. mutt mitt
9. laps lips	10. chin chun	11. crab crib	12. watch witch
13. twig twug	14. fan fin	15. wig wag	16. bib bub

Words with -in

Read the words in the box.
Write a word from the box to complete each sentence.

chin	fin	Pin	spin	twin	win

_____

1. I like to watch the top _____ .

_____

_____

2. The fish has a big _____ .

_____

_____

3. She has a _____ sister.

_____

_____

4. The team will _____ the game.

_____

_____

5. The man has hair on his _____ .

_____

_____

6. _____ the tail on the donkey.

Words with -ig

Name_____ Date _____

Read the words in the box.
Write a word from the box to complete each sentence.

big	dig	jig	pig	twig	wig

_____

1. Did you see the _____ roll in the mud?

_____

2. I saw the little elf dance a _____ .

_____

3. Does the bald witch wear a _____ ?

_____

4. Let's _____ a hole to plant the tree.

_____

5. The pretty bird sat on a _____ .

_____

6. A _____ dog jumped the gate.

Name_____ Date _____

The word **cup** has the short **u** sound.

Say the name of each picture. Color the pictures in each row that have the short **u** sound.

c<u>u</u>p

1.

2.

3.

4.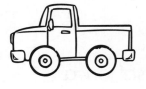

5.

Short Vowel u

Name_____ Date _____

The word **up** has the short **u** sound.

Say the name of each picture.
Circle the word that names the picture.

up

1. 	2. 	3. 	4. 
bug bag	**deck duck**	**cub cab**	**nut net**
5. 	6. 	7. 	8. 
jig jug	**rag rug**	**sun sin**	**cup cap**
9. 	10. 	11. 	12.
tub tib	**gem gum**	**cat cut**	**drum drom**
13. 	14. 	15. 	16.
sib sub	**hog hug**	**thumb thimb**	**cuff caff**

43

Words with -ub

Read the words in the box.
Write a word from the box to complete each sentence.

cub	rub	scrub	stub	sub	tub

_____

1. The baby _____ sleeps in a cave.

_____

2. The _____ moves underwater.

_____

3. Jan put the pup into the _____ to bathe it.

_____

4. Mom will _____ the pan.

_____

5. The genie will come if you _____ the lamp.

_____

6. It hurts to _____ your toe.

Words with -ug

Name_____ Date _____

Read the words in the box.
Write a word from the box to complete each sentence.

bug	hug	tug	mug	plug	rug

_____

1. The pup likes to _____ on the rope.

_____

2. Wipe your feet on the _____ .

_____

3. Dad will _____ in the lamp.

_____

4. Mom drinks coffee out of a _____ .

_____

5. Yuk! There is a _____ on my cup!

_____

6. I like to give my mom a _____ .

Short Vowel o

Name_____ Date _____

The word **pot** has the short **o** sound.

p<u>o</u>t

Say the name of each picture.
Color the pictures in each row that have the short **o** sound.

1.

2.

3.

4.

5.

Short Vowel o

Name_____ Date_____

The word **sock** has the short **o** sound.

s<u>o</u>ck

Say the name of each picture.
Circle the word that names the picture.

1. ox   ax

2.  bix   box

3.  map   mop

4.  lock   lick

5.  clack   clock

6.  pet   pot

7. top   tap

8.  knit   knot

9. pop   pip

10. hip   hop

11. cat   cot

12. jag   jog

13. frig   frog

14.  leg   log

15.  doll   dill

16.  rock   ruck

47

Words with -og

Name_____ Date _____

Read the words in the box.
Write a word from the box to complete each sentence.

dog	fog	frog	hog	jog	log

_____

1. My _____ barks at the mailman.

_____

2. I like to _____ around the block.

_____

3. Can you jump over that _____ ?

_____

4. Tom found a _____ in his yard.

_____

5. The fat _____ won first prize at the County Fair.

_____

6. The _____ was very thick in the morning.

Words with -op

Name_____ Date _____

Read the words in the box.
Write a word from the box to complete each sentence.

drop	hop	mop	pop	shop	stop

_____

1. Can you _____ on one foot?

_____

2. The car will _____ for walkers.

_____

3. Cindy loves to _____ .

_____

4. The red balloon did not _____ .

_____

5. The janitor will _____ the floor.

_____

6. Did the player _____ the ball?

Short Vowel e

Name_____ Date _____

The word **bell** has the short **e** sound.

b**e**ll

Say the name of each picture.
Circle the pictures in each row that have the short **e** sound.

1.

2.

3.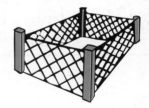

4.

5.

Short Vowel e

Name_____ Date _____

The word **egg** has the short **e** sound.

Say the name of each picture.
Circle the word that names the picture.

egg

Unit 2

1.  **bid bed**	2.  **leg lag**	3.  **ball bell**	4.  **tent tant**
5.  **balt belt**	6.  **well will**	7.  **twelve twulve**	8.  **nat net**
9.  **pun pen**	10.  **nast nest**	11.  **desk duck**	12.  **pat pet**
13.  **driss dress**	14.  **man men**	15.  **jat jet**	16.  **web wib**

Words with -et

Name_____ Date _____

Read the words in the box.
Write a word from the box to complete each sentence.

| bet | jet | met | pet | wet | yet |

_____

1. Sam has a _____ turtle.

_____

2. She _____ me at the store.

_____

3. The _____ flew high in the sky.

_____

4. I did not clean my room _____ .

_____

5. It is so much fun getting _____ .

_____

6. I'll _____ I can run faster than you.

52

Words with -en

Name_____ Date _____

Read the words in the box.
Write a word from the box to complete each sentence.

Ben	**hen**	**pen**	**ten**	**then**	**When**

_____
- - - - - - - - - - - - - -
1. The farmer fed his _____ .

_____

_____
- - - - - - - - - - - - -
2. I have _____ cents.

_____

_____
- - - - - - - - - - - -
3. _____ are we going to Grandma's house?

_____

_____
- - - - - - - - - - - -
4. A pig got out of the _____ .

_____

_____
- - - - - - - - - - -
5. I will eat lunch, and _____ I will watch T.V.

_____

_____
- - - - - - - - - - - -
6. _____ likes to play soccer.

Word Family Practice

Name_____ Date_____

Read each sentence. Circle the word that best completes the sentence. Write the word on the line.

1. Fran lost her _____ rabbit.	**Pat** **pet** **pig**
2. The man can _____ a hole.	**big** **jig** **dig**
3. The little _____ sat on the rock.	**mug** **hop** **frog**
4. Dad will buy a new red _____ .	**rat** **set** **van**
5. The _____ went down to the bottom of the ocean.	**sub** **tan** **cub**
6. _____ will we go to the zoo?	**Men** **When** **That**
7. Tom likes to _____ across the rocks.	**hop** **mop** **win**

54

Long Vowels with Silent e

Name_____ Date _____

When silent **e** is added to some words, the first vowel makes a **long** sound.

can   can**e**

Say the name of each picture. Add **e** at the end of each word. Then circle the picture of the new word.

1. **cap**    cap_____

2. **tap**    tap_____

3. **pin**    pin_____

4. **tub**    tub_____

Read each word.
Write two words from the box to complete each sentence.

plan
plane
not
note

5. The _____ can _____ fly today.

6. I _____ to write a _____ .

Long Vowel a

Name_____ Date _____

Say the name of each picture.
Circle the word that names the picture. Then write the word.

1. **gate**
   gas
   _____
   _ _ _ _ _ _ _
   _____

2. **plane**
   pan
   _____
   _ _ _ _ _ _ _
   _____

3. **rat**
   rake
   _____
   _ _ _ _ _ _ _
   _____

4. **lake**
   lamp
   _____
   _ _ _ _ _ _ _
   _____

5. **tag**
   tape
   _____
   _ _ _ _ _ _ _
   _____

6. **snap**
   snake
   _____
   _ _ _ _ _ _ _
   _____

7. **cast**
   cake
   _____
   _ _ _ _ _ _ _
   _____

8. **skate**
   scat
   _____
   _ _ _ _ _ _ _
   _____

9. **cane**
   can
   _____
   _ _ _ _ _ _ _
   _____

10. **cave**
    cane
    _____
    _ _ _ _ _ _ _
    _____

11. **wag**
    wave
    _____
    _ _ _ _ _ _ _
    _____

12. **cap**
    cape
    _____
    _ _ _ _ _ _ _
    _____

56

Long Vowel a

Name_____ Date _____

The **long a** in the word **train** is spelled **ai**.

tr**ai**n

Write **ai** to finish each word. Read the words.

1.

sn___l

2.

p___l

3.

t___l

4.

br___d

5.

s___l

6.

m___l

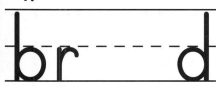

7.

r___n

8.

n___l

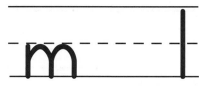

9.

p___nt

57

Unit 3

Long Vowel a

Name_____ Date _____

The **long a** in the word **tray** is spelled **ay**.

Read the words.
Write a word from the box to complete each sentence.

tr**ay**

day	**gray**	**hay**	**May**	**pay**	**stay**

_____
- - - - - - - - - - -

1. The black horse eats _____ .

_____
- - - - - - - - - - -

2. He will _____ for the candy.

_____
- - - - - - - - - - -

3. Our little _____ cat is lost.

_____
- - - - - - - - - - -

4. What _____ are we going to Grandma's house?

_____
- - - - - - - - - - -

5. _____ I please have a glass of milk?

_____
- - - - - - - - - - -

6. We must _____ here and wait for Mom.

Long Vowel a

Name_____ Date _____

Say the name of each picture.
Write a word for the second picture that rhymes.

1.

_____ _____

cake

2.

_____ _____

gray

3.

_____ _____

trail

4.

_____ _____

cave

5.

_____ _____

jay

6.

_____ _____

chain

Long Vowel i

Name_____ Date _____

The word **slide** has the **long i** sound.

Say the name of each picture. Circle the pictures in each row that have the **long i** sound.

sl<u>i</u>de

1.

2.

3.

4.

5.

Long Vowel i

Name_____ Date _____

The word **nine** has the **long i** sound.

Say the name of each picture.
Circle the word that names the picture.

n<u>i</u>ne

1.  fine five	2.  mice mine	3.  slip slide	4.  dive dig
5.  hide hive	6.  pin pie	7.  book bike	8.  dice does
9.  kite kit	10.  dim dime	11.  bride bread	12. pick price
13. Vinny vine	14. turn tire	15. tie top	16.  pipe pile

Long Vowel i

Say the name of each picture. Write a word for the second picture that rhymes. Use the words in the box.

| bride | dime | hive | kite | mice | tie |

1.
white _____

2.
pie _____

3.
lime _____

4.
dive _____

5.
price _____

6.
slide _____

Long Vowel i

Read the words.
Write a word from the box to complete each sentence.

bite	hike	line	mine	time	wipe

_____
\- \- \- \- \- \- \- \- \- \- \-

1. We went for a _____ in the mountains.

_____
\- \- \- \- \- \- \- \- \- \- \-

2. Write your name on the _____ .

_____
\- \- \- \- \- \- \- \- \- \- \-

3. What _____ do you have to leave?

_____
\- \- \- \- \- \- \- \- \- \- \-

4. Please _____ the table after eating lunch.

_____
\- \- \- \- \- \- \- \- \- \- \-

5. Someone took a _____ out of my sandwich.

_____
\- \- \- \- \- \- \- \- \- \- \-

6. That video is _____ , not yours.

Unit 3

Long Vowel u

Name_____ Date _____

The word **fruit** has the **long u** sound.

Say the name of each picture. Circle the pictures in each row that have the **long u** sound.

fr<u>ui</u>t

1.

2.
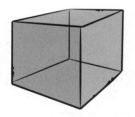   

3.

4.
 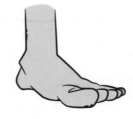  

Long Vowel u

Name_____ Date _____

Say the name of each picture.
Fill in the circle next to the word that names the picture.

1.
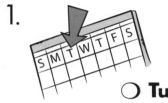
- ○ Tusk
- ○ Tuesday
- ○ Tune

2.
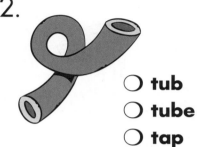
- ○ tub
- ○ tube
- ○ tap

3.
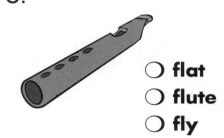
- ○ flat
- ○ flute
- ○ fly

4.

- ○ cub
- ○ cube
- ○ clock

5.

- ○ clap
- ○ club
- ○ clue

6.

- ○ juice
- ○ jump
- ○ junk

7.

- ○ bring
- ○ bruise
- ○ brush

8.

- ○ frog
- ○ frame
- ○ fruit

9.

- ○ mule
- ○ must
- ○ milk

10.

- ○ top
- ○ tug
- ○ tune

11.

- ○ gum
- ○ glue
- ○ grab

12.

- ○ sun
- ○ suit
- ○ sip

Long Vowel u

Name_____ Date _____

Read the words. Write a word from the box to name each picture.

| bruise clue cruise cube flute fruit |
| glue juice prune rude suit tube |

1. _____

2. _____

3. _____

4. _____

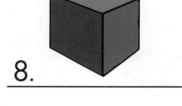

5. _____

6. _____

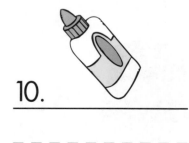

7. _____

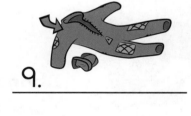

8. _____

9. _____

10. _____

11. _____

12. _____

Long Vowel u

Name_____ Date _____

Read each sentence. Circle the word that best completes the sentence.
Write the word on the line.

_____ - - - - - - - - - - 1. I can play a _____ on my flute.	**tune** **rule** **use**
_____ - - - - - - - - - - 2. My birthday is in the month of _____ .	**Tuesday** **June** **Ruth**
_____ - - - - - - - - - - 3. She will wear her new _____ dress.	**cube** **blue** **dude**
_____ - - - - - - - - - - 4. Do you want to go for a _____ ride?	**prune** **hue** **mule**
_____ - - - - - - - - - - 5. The library book is _____ today.	**due** **tube** **cute**
_____ - - - - - - - - - - 6. Is that story _____ or made up?	**blue** **glue** **true**
_____ - - - - - - - - - - 7. Mom put an ice _____ in my glass.	**clue** **cube** **cruise**

Name_____ Date _____

The word **coat** has the **long o** sound.

Say the name of each picture. Color the pictures in each row that have the **long o** sound.

c<u>oa</u>t

1.

2.

3.

4.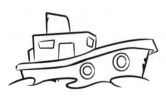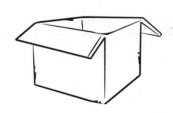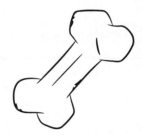

Long Vowel o

Name_____ Date _____

The word **hoe** has the **long o** sound.

Say the name of each picture.
Circle the word that names the picture.

h**oe**

1.  **doe down**	2.  **cane cone**	3.  **note nut**
4.  **coal could**	5.  **glob globe**	6. 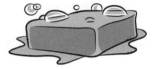 **soap sob**
7.  **cot coat**	8.  **home hut**	9.  **test toast**
10.  **toe town**	11.  **rob robe**	12.  **boat bop**

69   © 2020 Twin Sisters IP, LLC. All Rights Reserved.

Long Vowel o

Name_____ Date _____

Read the words. Write a word from the box to name each picture.

| boat cone doze hole nose pole |
| road rope rose snow stove toad |

1. _____

2. _____

3. _____

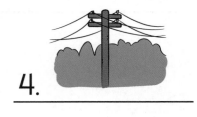

4. _____

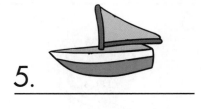

5. _____

6. _____

7. _____

8. _____

9. _____

10. _____

11. _____

12. _____

Long Vowel o

Name_____ Date _____

Read each sentence. Circle the word that best completes the sentence.
Write the word on the line.

_____ - - - - - - - - - - 1. We will _____ to the store.	**no** **go** **so**
_____ - - - - - - - - - - 2. Did the wind _____ the tree down?	**mow** **blow** **throw**
_____ - - - - - - - - - - 3. I like to sleep in my _____ bed.	**own** **blown** **grown**
_____ - - - - - - - - - - 4. I _____ we can play outside today.	**nose** **hope** **slow**
_____ - - - - - - - - - - 5. _____ crayons belong to Joan.	**Those** **Post** **Toe**
_____ - - - - - - - - - - 6. I want to be a _____ for Halloween.	**grown** **glow** **ghost**
_____ - - - - - - - - - - 7. Mom _____ us to the baseball game.	**vote** **snow** **drove**

Unit 3

Long Vowel e

The word **leaf** has the **long e** sound.

Say the name of each picture. Color the pictures in each row that have the **long e** sound.

le**a**f

1.

2.

3.

4.

5.

Long Vowel e

Name_____ Date _____

The word **feet** has the **long e** sound.

f**ee**t

Say the name of each picture. Circle the word that names the picture.

1. 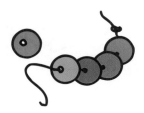 **bunk** **bead**	2.  **peel** **pet**	3.  **read** **red**
4.  **puppy** **peach**	5.  **meal** **melt**	6. **queen** **quick**
7.  **jeep** **jump**	8.  **shirt** **sheep**	9.  **loaf** **leaf**
10.  **smell** **seal**	11.  **meat** **mile**	12.  **seat** **sell**

Long Vowel e

Name_____ Date _____

Say the name of each picture.
Write a word for the second picture that rhymes.

1.

_____   _____
sea

2.

_____   _____
beet

3.

_____   _____
tree

4.

_____   _____
beach

5.

_____   _____
meal

6.

_____   _____
heel

Long Vowel e

Name_____ Date _____

Read the words.
Write a word from the box to complete each sentence.

| clean | dream | knee | seed | She | tea |

_____
- - - - - - - - - - - - -
1. We drank _____ and ate cookies at the party.

_____
- - - - - - - - - -
2. The boy had a scary _____ .

_____
- - - - - - - - -
3. _____ is my best friend.

_____
- - - - - - - - - -
4. I hurt my _____ while riding my bike.

_____
- - - - - - - - -
5. The tiny _____ grew into a giant beanstalk!

_____
- - - - - - - - - -
6. I will help Dad _____ the garage.

y as a Vowel

The letter **y** in **bunny** makes the **long e** sound.

The letter **y** in **fly** makes the **long i** sound.

Say each picture name. If it ends like **bunny**, write an **e** on the line. If it ends like **fly**, write an **i** on the line.

1. **pony**

2. **sky**

3. **dry**

4. **funny**

5. **cry**

6. **city**

7. **family**

8. **happy**

9. **fry**

y as a Vowel

Name_____ Date _____

Read each sentence. Circle the word that best completes the sentence. Write the word on the line.

1. My _____ is big.	**funny** **family** **fussy**
2. The _____ is pretty.	**sky** **shy** **sly**
3. Did you _____ the wet dish?	**doll** **dry** **by**
4. It is _____ to fry an egg.	**easy** **each** **dizzy**
5. The plant is _____ dry.	**hairy** **ready** **very**
6. _____ is he sleepy?	**Why** **Try** **Fly**
7. The silly puppy has _____ paws.	**spy** **muddy** **merry**

R Blends

Name_____ Date_____

Read the words. Notice the sound that the two letters at the beginning of each word make.

drum 　　**fr**og 　　**gr**apes

 crab　　 **br**ick　　 **pr**ize　　 **tr**ee

Color the pictures in each row that have the same beginning sound as the first picture.

1. |

2.  |

3.  |

4.  |

5.  |

R Blends

Name_____ Date_____

Read the words in the box.
Write the correct word from the box to name each picture.

bride	bridge	brush	crab	crib	drill
drip	frame	frog	grapes	pretzel	tree

1. _____

2. _____

3. _____

4. _____

5. _____

6. _____

7. _____

8. _____

9. _____

10. _____

11. _____

12. _____

Unit 4

L Blends

Name_____ Date_____

flower   **bl**ock   **cl**oud   **pl**ug   **gl**ass   **sl**eeve

Color the pictures in each row that have the same beginning sound as the first picture.

1.

  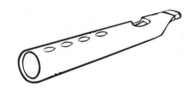 

2.

3.

4.

Name_____ Date_____

Read the words in the box.
Write the correct word from the box to name each picture.

| blanket | block | clip | clue | flag | flower |
| glove | glue | plant | plate | slate | slip |

1. _____

_ _ _ _ _ _ _ _ _ _ _

2. _____

_ _ _ _ _ _ _ _ _ _ _

3. _____

_ _ _ _ _ _ _ _ _ _ _

4. _____

_ _ _ _ _ _ _ _ _ _ _

5. _____

_ _ _ _ _ _ _ _ _ _ _

6. _____

_ _ _ _ _ _ _ _ _ _ _

7. _____

_ _ _ _ _ _ _ _ _ _ _

8. _____

_ _ _ _ _ _ _ _ _ _ _

9. _____

_ _ _ _ _ _ _ _ _ _ _

10. _____

_ _ _ _ _ _ _ _ _ _ _

11. _____

_ _ _ _ _ _ _ _ _ _ _

12. _____

_ _ _ _ _ _ _ _ _ _ _

Unit 4

S Blends

Name_____ Date_____

smile   **sn**ake   **st**ool   **sp**ill   **sw**im   **sk**ate

Say the name of each picture.
Circle the letters that stand for the beginning sound.

1. 	2.  	3. 	4. 
sp **sw**	**sm** **sp**	**sn** **st**	**sn** **sp**

5. 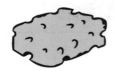	6.  	7. 	8.
sp **st**	**st** **sw**	**sw** **sm**	**sn** **sw**

9. 	10. 	11.	12. 
sn **sp**	**sn** **sw**	**sp** **st**	**sm** **sn**

13. 	14. 	15.	16. 
sk **st**	**sw** **sk**	**sp** **st**	**st** **sc**

S Blends

Name_____ Date_____

Read the words in the box. Say the name of each picture.
Write the word from the box that names the picture.

skate	smile	snail	snake	sniff	spell
stamp	stick	stir	swan	swim	swing

1. _____

2. _____

3. _____

4. _____

5. _____

6. _____

7. _____

8. _____

9. _____

10. _____

11. _____

12. _____

Unit 4

Ending Blends

Name_____ Date_____

Say the name of each picture.
Circle the letters that stand for the ending sound.

1.	2.	3.	4.
nt **ck**	**ng** **nd**	**nt** **ck**	**nd** **ng**

5.	6.	7.	8.
ck **ng**	**nt** **ck**	**nt** **ng**	**nd** **ng**

9.	10.	11.	12.
ng **ck**	**nd** **ng**	**nd** **ng**	**ck** **ng**

13.	14.	15.	16.
nt **ck**	**ck** **sk**	**nd** **nt**	**ck** **nt**

17.	18.	19.	20.
st **sp**	**nd** **mp**	**sk** **ck**	**sk** **nt**

Beginning and Ending th

Name_____ Date_____

The beginning sound in **thirteen** **13** is spelled **th**.

The ending sound in **moth** is spelled **th**.

Read the words in the box.
Write a word from the box to complete each sentence.

bath	path	thorn	three	tooth

1. The cat has a _____ stuck in its paw.

2. My little brother is _____ years old.

3. It is time to take a _____ .

4. Beth has a loose _____ .

5. We walked on the _____ in the park.

Beginning wh

Name_____ Date_____

The beginning sound in **wheel** is spelled **wh**.

Read the words in the box.
Write a word from the box to complete each sentence.

<u>**wh**</u>eel

whale **What** **wheat** **When** **Where**

1. The farmer grew _____ on his farm.

2. _____ time is my ballet practice?

3. A _____ is a mammal.

4. _____ is my book?

5. _____ will Dad be home?

Beginning and Ending sh

The beginning sound in **shoe** is spelled **sh**.

The ending sound in **dish** is spelled **sh**.

Read the words in the box.
Write a word from the box to complete each sentence.

brush	bush	shine	shovel	trash

_____

1. Use a _____ to dig the hole.

_____

2. Grandma planted a _____ between the trees.

_____

3. My job is to take out the _____ .

_____

4. The stars _____ so bright at night.

_____

5. My sister likes to _____ her long hair.

Beginning and Ending ch

Name_____ Date_____

The beginning sound in **chair** is spelled **ch**.

The ending sound in **branch** is spelled **ch**.

Read the words in the box.
Write a word from the box to complete each sentence.

bench	cheese	chicken	chop	inch

1. I helped my Dad _____ wood.

2. Do you like _____ on your hamburger?

3. The man sat on the _____ and rested.

4. I grew an _____ this year!

5. The _____ laid an egg.

Digraph kn

Name_____ Date_____

The beginning sound in **knot** is spelled **kn**.

knot

Read the words in the box.
Write a word from the box to complete each sentence.

knee   knew   knight   knit   knock

1. Did you hear the _____ at the door?

2. I scraped my _____ while rollerblading.

3. The brave _____ saved the princess.

4. I _____ all the answers yesterday.

5. Grandma will _____ the baby a hat.

Digraph Practice

Name_____ Date_____

Say the name of each picture.
Fill in the circle next to the word that names the picture.

1. ○ cheese ○ shell ○ thick	**2.** ○ check ○ shed ○ whale	**3.** ○ chip ○ shop ○ thumb
4. ○ check ○ shack ○ thin	**5.** ○ chick ○ shark ○ what	**6.** ○ chin ○ shell ○ wheel
7. ○ bath ○ bench ○ bush	**8.** ○ fast ○ fish ○ five	**9.** ○ bat ○ bath ○ beach
10. ○ tent ○ thin ○ tooth	**11.** ○ brush ○ buck ○ show	**12.** ○ wand ○ watch ○ wish

-ed Ending

Name_____ Date_____

Read each sentence. Add **-ed** to the word below the blank and write the new word to complete the sentence.

_____
- - - - - - - - - - - - - -

1. Our family _____ hard today.
      (work)

_____
- - - - - - - - - - - - - -

2. Sally _____ the gate.
      (fix)

_____
- - - - - - - - - - - - - -

3. Ted _____ the van.
      (wash)

_____
- - - - - - - - - - - - - -

4. Bobby _____ the grass.
      (mow)

_____
- - - - - - - - - - - - - -

5. Sara _____ flowers in the garden.
      (plant)

_____
- - - - - - - - - - - - - -

6. Then we all _____ .
      (rest)

-ing Ending

Name_____ Date_____

Read each sentence. Add **-ing** to the word below the blank and write the new word to complete the sentence.

_____

1. Carla is _____ the seeds.
   (water)

_____

2. She is _____ for them to sprout.
   (wait)

_____

3. The seeds will be _____ soon.
   (grow)

_____

4. Carla likes _____ the beans.
   (pick)

_____

5. Mom is _____ bean soup.
   (cook)

_____

6. We like _____ Mom's bean soup!
   (eat)

-ed and -ing Ending

Name_____ Date_____

Read each sentence. Circle the correct ending for the word under the blank to complete the sentence. Write the new word.

1. Mom _____ Ann's toy. (fix)	**ed** **ing**
2. My teacher _____ me with my math. (help)	**ed** **ing**
3. Lisa is _____ a dog. (draw)	**ed** **ing**
4. Pat is _____ up the hill. (walk)	**ed** **ing**
5. It _____ all day. (rain)	**ed** **ing**
6. The pups are _____ . (bark)	**ed** **ing**

Unit 5

93

High-Frequency Sight Words

Name_____ Date_____

Read the words in the box.
Write a word from the box to complete each sentence.

after	**brown**	**did**	**find**	**from**	**give**	**help**
know	**made**	**round**	**soon**	**that**	**under**	**your**

_____

1. I got a letter _____ my friend.

_____

2. I _____ a vase out of clay.

_____

3. Is that _____ cup of milk or mine?

_____

4. I found my socks _____ my bed.

_____

5. Pretty _____ we will go to the show.

_____

6. Joe likes to _____ Dad fix the car.

High-Frequency Sight Words

Name_____ Date_____

Unscramble the letters to make a word.
Use the words at the bottom if you need help.

1. newt _____

2. tawh _____

3. nfid _____

4. nmya _____

5. own _____

6. agnia _____

7. eewr _____

8. hten _____

9. umch _____

10. cmoe _____

11. csabeeu _____

12. ervo _____

13. eliv _____

14. wnhe _____

now	then	find	when	what	over	were	live
went	many	come	again	much	because		

Unit 5

Compound Words

Name_____ Date_____

A **compound word** is made from two or more shorter words.

⭐ + 🐟 = **starfish** ⭐

---

butterfly   football   handbag   mailbox   pancake   raincoat

---

Say the name of each picture. Put the names together to make a compound word. Write the new word.

1. 🖐 + 🛍 = _____

2. 🦶 + ⚽ = _____

3. ☁ + 🧥 = _____

4. 🧈 + 🪰 = _____

5. ✉ + 📦 = _____

6. 🍳 + 🎂 = _____

Compound Words

Name_____ Date_____

Say the name of each picture. Put the names together to make a compound word. Write the new word.

1.  **+** **=**  _____
   snow   +   man   =   _____

2. **+**  **=**  _____
   pin   +   wheel   =   _____

3. **+** ... **=**  _____
   tea   +   pot   =   _____

4.  **+** ... **=** ... _____
   cup   +   cake   =   _____

5. **+** **=**   _____
   dog   +   house   =   _____

6. **+** **=** _____
   star   +   fish   =   _____

Contractions

Name_____ Date_____

A contraction is a way of putting two words together and making them shorter.	Sometimes the first word changes.
do + not = don't **Do not** go in my room. **Don't** go in my room.	**will + not = won't** I **will not** go in your room. I **won't** go in your room.

Read the contractions. Write the contraction that can be used in place of each pair of words.

aren't	**can't**	**didn't**	**doesn't**	**don't**
hasn't	**haven't**	**isn't**	**weren't**	**won't**

1. did not _____

2. has not _____

3. can not _____

4. were not _____

5. have not _____

6. is not _____

7. will not _____

8. are not _____

9. do not _____

10. does not _____

Contractions

Name_____ Date_____

Read the first sentence.
Write the correct contraction to complete the second sentence.

We are going to the beach!
_____

- -

1. _____ going to the beach!

They are in the water.
_____

- -

2. _____ in the water.

You are late for lunch.
_____

- -

3. _____ late for lunch.

You are reading!
_____

- -

4. _____ reading!

We are going to the movies.
_____

- -

5. _____ going to the movies.

They are riding their bikes.
_____

- -

6. _____ riding their bikes.

Unit 5

Contractions

A contraction is a way of putting two words together and making them shorter.	**I + will = I'll** **I will** eat my lunch. **I'll** eat my lunch.

Read the contractions.
Write the two words that make up each contraction.

1. we'll _____ _____

2. they'll _____ _____

3. he'll _____ _____

4. I'll _____ _____

5. it'll _____ _____

6. you'll _____ _____

7. who'll _____ _____

Contractions

Name_____ Date_____

| she is = she's | it is = it's | he is = he's. |

Read the sentences.
Write a contraction to replace each group of underlined words.

It is a nice day to go to the zoo.

_____

1. _____ a nice day to go the zoo.

She is watching the polar bears.

_____

2. _____ watching the polar bears.

He is feeding the sea lions.

_____

3. _____ feeding the sea lions.

He is talking to the parrots.

_____

4. _____ talking to the parrots.

It is hot. Let's get some ice cream!

_____

5. _____ hot. Let's get some ice cream!

Unit 5

Synonyms

Name_____ Date_____

Words with the same or almost the
same meaning are called **synonyms**.

Close and **shut** are synonyms.

Read the first word in each row. Circle the synonym.

1.	car	bike	auto	plow
2.	small	little	big	huge
3.	build	hammer	make	ladder
4.	big	tiny	dog	large
5.	yell	talk	shout	girl
6.	night	evening	day	moon
7.	look	sleep	see	jump
8.	fast	run	slow	quick

Antonyms

Name_____ Date_____

Antonyms are words with opposite meanings.
New and **old** are antonyms.

new   old

Read the first word in each row. Circle the antonym.

1.	over	up	jog	under
2.	full	big	empty	take
3.	fat	thin	tall	old
4.	big	large	sun	little
5.	strong	sad	weak	cry
6.	in	door	come	out
7.	dry	wet	hot	wash
8.	hot	cook	cold	fire

Unit 5

Adjectives

Name_____ Date_____

Adjectives tell more about nouns.
They can answer these questions:

What kind?　　　　　　　How many?
fuzzy bears　　　　　　**two** bears

What color?
brown bears

Read each sentence.
Circle the correct adjective and write it to complete the sentence.

1. This is a _____ flower.
　　　pretty　　grow

2. The _____ birds sing.
　　　black　　beak

3. I see _____ mice.
　　bug　　tiny

4. His mitt is _____.
　　　new　　up

5. She has _____ hair.
　　long　　smile

6. He has _____ sisters.
　　　fire　　four

7. The _____ bus is red.
　　big　　tires

8. The dogs are _____.
　　　tail　　small

Synonyms, Antonyms, and Adjectives

Name_____ Date_____

Read the words in the box.
Write a word from the box to answer each riddle.

back crispy day down five hop long unhappy

1. I am the opposite of front. _____

2. I mean the same as sad. _____

3. I am the kind of pizza crust you have. _____

4. I am the opposite of short. _____

5. I mean the same as jump. _____

6. I can tell how many fingers you have. _____

7. I am the opposite of up. _____

8. I am the opposite of night. _____

Unit 5

Story Sequence

Name_____ Date_____

The pictures in each row tell a story, but they are out of order. Write **1** by the event that happened first, **2** by the event that happened next, and **3** by the event that happened last.

1.

2.

3.

Story Sequence

These pictures tell a story, but they are out of order.
Number them from **1** to **6** to show the order of what happened.

Unit 6

Main Idea

Name_____ Date_____

The **main idea** of a story is its most important part.

Each group of pictures tells a story.
Look at the pictures and circle the sentence that tells the main idea.

1.

The birthday party was fun.   Jason got a bike for his birthday.

No one had fun at the party.   Jason's cake was big.

2.

Sue gave away three kittens.   Sue does not like kittens.

Sue kept all the kittens.   The kittens were gray.

Main Idea

Name_____ Date_____

Read each story.
Fill in the circle next to the sentence that tells the main idea.

1. Tracy sees that it is raining. She puts on boots. She puts on a raincoat. She puts on a hat. Now she is ready.

    ○ **Tracy dresses for a rainy day.**
    ○ **Tracy takes a long time to get ready.**

2. Paint is coming off the old house. The windows are broken. The front door is loose. The roof has big holes.

    ○ **The old house is nice.**
    ○ **The old house needs to be fixed.**

3. Joey had a good day. He found a dime on the ground. He got an A on his work. A friend chose him for her team. His mom gave him a big hug.

    ○ **Joey has lots of friends.**
    ○ **Joey had a good day.**

Story Map

Read the story. Then, fill in the story map.

It is easy to make a cheese sandwich. First, spread butter on two slices of bread. Next, put some cheese between the bread slices. Cut the sandwich in half. Now it is ready to eat!

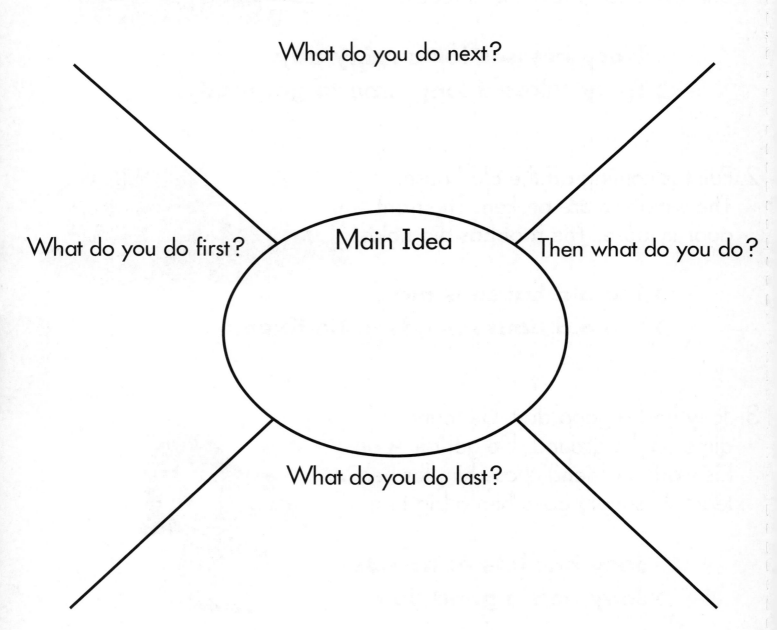

What do you do next?

What do you do first?

Main Idea

Then what do you do?

What do you do last?

Predicting Outcomes

Name_____ Date_____

Read each story beginning. Then, fill in the circle next to the sentence ending that makes the most sense.

1. Brendon woke up excited and happy. The sun was shining. It was a perfect day for a trip to the beach. After a few seconds, Brendon

   ○ **jumped out of bed.**
   ○ **rolled over and went back to sleep.**

2. Maggie knew a storm was coming. The sky was gray. A strong wind began to blow. Thunder rolled. Maggie decided to

   ○ **go outside and play.**
   ○ **stay inside with her family.**

3. Dee was ready for the dance show. She had done her steps over and over. Before the show, she felt sure of herself. She smiled as she came onto the stage. Then Dee

   ○ **forgot all the dance steps.**
   ○ **did the dance well.**

Unit 6

Drawing Conclusions

Name_____ Date_____

Look for clues in each picture. Circle the sentence that tells what most likely happened between the two pictures in each row.

1.

The girl threw the ball at the window.

The girl batted the ball through the window.

Someone in the house broke the window.

2.

The sun came out.

It got colder.

Someone pushed the snowman over.

3.

The boy sawed the branch off.

Lightning struck the tree.

The branch broke off.

Inferences

Use the picture clues to guess what is happening.
Circle the guess that fits the clues.

1. This boy just won a race.

    This boy just lost a race.

---

2.    The show is about to begin.

    The show is over.

---

3. It is very quiet.

    The girl hears loud noises.

---

4.    Sam just ate a jelly sandwich.

    Sam has not eaten all day.

---

5. This girl likes carrots.

    This girl does not like carrots.

---

6.    Today is windy.

    There is no wind today.

Unit 6

Reading Practice

Name_____ Date_____

Read Joy's story. Then, fill in the circle next to the correct answer.

Our family went to town to see the parade. At about noon, we joined a big crowd. My brother Roy was in the band. Dad pointed out where he was. We could all see him and we shouted and waved. The band music sounded good and loud.

The parade lasted about a half an hour. We all enjoyed it. If I had my choice, I would see a parade every day.

1. What is the main idea of the story?
   ○ The band music was loud.
   ○ Joy's family waved to Roy.
   ○ Joy's family saw a parade.

2. Where did Joy's family go to see the parade?
   ○ in town
   ○ to school
   ○ to a football game

3. What did Joy have to say about the band music?
   ○ It was bad.
   ○ The drums were too loud.
   ○ It was good and loud.

4. What do you think the family will do the next time there is a parade?
   ○ They will stay home.
   ○ They will go to the parade.
   ○ They will go to the zoo.

Reading Practice

Name_____ Date_____

Read the story. Then, fill in the circle next to the correct answer.

It is fun to shop in the city. Mom and I get on the bus at Oak Street. First, we pass the school. Then, the bus takes us over a bridge. Soon, we see a tall building with a red flag. We pass lots of people walking. At Main Street, the bus driver stops the bus and Mom and I step off. Now it is time to shop!

1. What is the main idea of the story?
   - ○ We see tall buildings.
   - ○ We ride the bus.
   - ○ Mom and I shop in the city.

2. What do Mom and I pass first?
   - ○ the school
   - ○ lots of people
   - ○ our home

3. Where does the bus stop?
   - ○ at the building
   - ○ at the school
   - ○ at Main Street

4. What do you think will happen next?
   - ○ Mom and I will go back home.
   - ○ Mom and I will go shopping.
   - ○ Mom and I will visit Grandma.

Capitalization

Name_____ Date_____

The first word in a sentence always begins with a **capital letter**.

The boys like to play catch.

↖ capital letter

Read each sentence. Fill in the circle next to the sentences that begin with a capital letter.

○ 1. That little mouse eats cheese.

○ 2. my Dad is fixing the car.

○ 3. Did you see the movie?

○ 4. I got a new bike for my birthday.

○ 5. he is playing with his truck.

○ 6. when will we go to the park?

○ 7. My dog likes to bark at the mailman.

○ 8. The teacher passed out the papers.

○ 9. the boat is on the lake.

○ 10. Julie will help bake cookies.

Capitalization

Name_____ Date_____

Underline the word that should be capitalized in each sentence. Then, rewrite the sentence correctly.

1. the baby is sleeping.

_____

_____

2. we are going to the park.

_____

_____

3. mom is cooking fish.

_____

_____

4. i am having a party.

_____

_____

5. a bee stung me.

_____

_____

6. today is a great day.

_____

_____

Unit 7

Punctuation

Name_____ Date_____

A sentence that tells something ends with a **period**.
It is called a **statement**.

My dog is black and white**.**

period

Read each sentence.
Fill in the circle next to the sentence that is written correctly.

○ 1. The boat can sail on the lake

○ 2. It is good to drink a lot of water.

○ 3. Today we played outside.

○ 4. I will help Dad rake the leaves.

○ 5. Patrick is my best friend

○ 6. The turtle sat on a rock.

○ 7. The cat naps on my bed

○ 8. Tyler gave his Mom a hug

○ 9. We watched a movie last night.

○ 10. Grandma read me a story.

Punctuation

Name_____ Date_____

Read each sentence. If it needs a period, add it.
Then, rewrite the sentence correctly.

1. The sky is blue

_____

- -

_____

2. Our team won the game.

_____

- -

_____

3. The puppy chewed my shoe.

_____

- -

_____

4. It is fun to fly a kite

_____

- -

_____

5. Please close the door.

_____

- -

_____

6. I like to paint

_____

- -

_____

Unit 7

Punctuation

Name_____ Date_____

A sentence that asks a **question** ends with a **question mark**.

Can you kick the ball**?**

question mark

Read each sentence.
Fill in the circle next to each sentence that asks a question.

○ 1. It will rain today.

○ 2. What is your name?

○ 3. I think he is at the door.

○ 4. Who won the game?

○ 5. He doesn't know your brother.

○ 6. Can I use your pencil?

○ 7. What time is it?

○ 8. You did not watch the video.

○ 9. Kangaroos live in Australia.

○ 10. Would you like an apple or an orange?

Punctuation

Name_____ Date_____

Read each sentence. If it needs a question mark, add it.
Then, rewrite the sentence correctly.

1. May I go with you

_____

- -

_____

2. How old are you?

_____

- -

_____

3. What are you doing

_____

- -

_____

4. Do you know how to get there?

_____

- -

_____

5. Are you leaving now?

_____

- -

_____

6. What is your favorite movie

_____

- -

_____

Punctuation

A sentence that shows **excitement** ends with an **exclamation point**.

Run**!**

exclamation point

Read each sentence.
Fill in the circle next to each sentence that shows excitement.

○ 1. Joshua can run one mile.

○ 2. Did you read that book?

○ 3. Watch out!

○ 4. Lindsey needs to clean her room.

○ 5. Ouch!

○ 6. That was a great game!

○ 7. This soup is hot!

○ 8. Can we play in the snow?

○ 9. Wow! You did a great job!

○ 10. It is very windy in Chicago.

Capitalization and Punctuation Practice

Name_____ Date_____

Rewrite each sentence using the correct capitalization and punctuation.

1. my favorite color is blue

_____

_ _

_____

2. can we watch a video

_____

_ _

_____

3. wow that building is tall

_____

_ _

_____

4. i am so hungry

_____

_ _

_____

5. dad is taking us to the park

_____

_ _

_____

6. are you feeling ill

_____

_ _

_____

Unit 7

Nouns

Name_____ Date_____

A word that names a person, place, or thing is called a **noun**.

mother
person

home
place

purse
thing

Read the words in the box.
Write the correct word from the box to name each picture.

| barn | bug | car | city | farmer | flower | girl | hat | shop |

1. _____

2. _____

3. _____

4. _____

5. _____

6. _____

7. _____

8. _____

9. _____

Proper Nouns

Name_____ Date _____

A **proper noun** is the name of an exact person, place, or thing.
Every **proper noun** begins with a capital letter.

United **S**tates   **J**une

Read each sentence and circle the proper noun that is not written
correctly. Rewrite the proper noun correctly.

_____

1. The train goes to boston. _____

2. I live on park road. _____

3. maria ran home fast. _____

4. Her birthday is in march. _____

5. That man lives in japan. _____

6. ken rides a red bike. _____

Unit 7

Plural Nouns

To make many nouns mean "more than one" add **s** at the end. Adding **s** makes a plural noun.

one bear

three bear**s**

Read each word in the box. If the word is plural, write it on the **Animals** list. If the word is not plural, write it on the **Animal** list.

birds cats dogs ducks frog horse lion pig rabbits tiger

Animal	**Animals**

Plural Nouns

Name_____ Date_____

A **plural noun** names "more than one."
Add **-es** to a noun ending in **s**, **x**, **ch**, or **sh** to make it **plural**.

one dress   two dress**es**   one fox   two fox**es**

Rewrite each noun, adding **-es** to make it plural.

1. match

_____

2. bus

_____

3. brush

_____

4. box

_____

5. six

_____

6. inch

_____

7. glass

_____

8. wish

_____

Unit 7

Verbs

A **verb** is a word that tells what a person or thing does.

The sun **<u>shines</u>**.

Circle the verb in each sentence.

1. Boats sail on the sea.

2. We run on the sandy beach.

3. A woman sits in the sun.

4. Our ice cream melts.

5. Waves come to the shore.

6. The girls play a game.

7. The boy throws a ball.

8. Dad dives into the water.

128

Verbs

A **verb** usually ends in **s** when it tells about only one person or thing. A **verb** usually does not end in **s** when it tells about more than one person or thing.

The star **twinkle<u>s</u>**.   Stars **twinkle**.

Read each sentence. Circle the correct verb to complete it.

1. The little bear_____ a spacesuit.
       wear   wears

2. Bears _____ into space today.
       go   goes

3. The bears _____ into the spaceship.
       get   gets

4. The big bear _____ pictures.
       take   takes

5. The little bear _____ into space.
       float   floats

6. The bears _____ at the planets.
       look   looks

Unit 7

Verbs

Name_____ Date_____

Choose the correct verb to complete each sentence. Write the verb.

_____

- - - - - - - - - - - - - - -

1. Tina _____ to the park.
    walks   walking

_____

- - - - - - - - - - - - - - -

2. Our class _____ the museum.
       visit   visited

_____

- - - - - - - - - - - - - - -

3. Jim _____ the TV show.
      watch   watches

_____

- - - - - - - - - - - - - - -

4. Mom is _____ the dishes.
      washed   washing

_____

- - - - - - - - - - - - - - -

5. Some children are _____ a picture.
           paint   painting

_____

- - - - - - - - - - - - - - -

6. The kitten _____ when it's happy.
       purrs   purring

Writing Sentences

Name_____ Date_____

Every sentence has two parts. The **naming part** is who or what is being talked about. The **action part** tells what a person or thing does or is.

The cat   plays with yarn.

naming part ➜   ↖ action part

Draw a line to match each naming part with an action part.

Naming Parts	**Action Parts**
The toy car	is open late.
The girls	bark loudly.
Snow	is tall.
My father	is falling on the tree.
The dogs	is broken.
That store	are best friends.

Write two of the sentences you made.

_____

1. _____

_____

2. _____

Unit 7

Noun and Verb Practice

Name_____ Date_____

Write a noun or verb from the box to complete each sentence.

ape	ball	bear	made	went	were

_____verb_____

- - - - - - - - - - - - - - - - - -

1. We _____ to the zoo.

_____noun_____

- - - - - - - - - - - - - - - - - -

2. I waved to the _____ .

_____verb_____

- - - - - - - - - - - - - - - -

3. The monkeys _____ me laugh.

_____noun_____

- - - - - - - - - - - - - - -

4. The _____ was asleep.

_____verb_____

- - - - - - - - - - - - - - -

5. The hippos _____ fat.

_____noun_____

- - - - - - - - - - - - - - -

6. A seal played with a _____ .

Addition Facts to 10

Name_____ Date_____

Write how many.

1.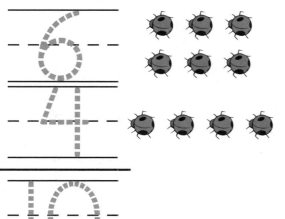

_____ in all

2.

_____ in all

3.

_____ in all

4.

_____ in all

5.

_____ in all

6.

_____ in all

Addition Number Sentences

Name_____ Date_____

Circle the correct number sentence.

1.

   3 + 7 = 10

   $\widetilde{3 + 6 = 9}$

2.

   5 + 4 = 9

   5 + 5 = 10

3.

   7 + 3 = 10

   8 + 2 = 10

4.

   6 + 3 = 9

   6 + 2 = 8

5.

   0 + 7 = 7

   6 + 1 = 7

6.

   3 + 6 = 9

   3 + 5 = 8

Addition Facts to 10

Name_____ Date_____

Add to find the sums.

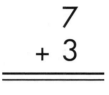

1.

$$\begin{array}{r} 7 \\ +\ 3 \\ \hline \end{array}$$
$$\begin{array}{r} 5 \\ +\ 4 \\ \hline \end{array}$$
$$\begin{array}{r} 2 \\ +\ 2 \\ \hline \end{array}$$
$$\begin{array}{r} 2 \\ +\ 7 \\ \hline \end{array}$$

2.

$$\begin{array}{r} 0 \\ +\ 9 \\ \hline \end{array}$$
$$\begin{array}{r} 5 \\ +\ 2 \\ \hline \end{array}$$
$$\begin{array}{r} 3 \\ +\ 6 \\ \hline \end{array}$$
$$\begin{array}{r} 1 \\ +\ 2 \\ \hline \end{array}$$

3.

$$\begin{array}{r} 2 \\ +\ 8 \\ \hline \end{array}$$
$$\begin{array}{r} 3 \\ +\ 5 \\ \hline \end{array}$$
$$\begin{array}{r} 6 \\ +\ 1 \\ \hline \end{array}$$
$$\begin{array}{r} 2 \\ +\ 3 \\ \hline \end{array}$$

Addition Facts to 10

Name_____ Date_____

Find the sums. Then use the code to color the picture.

10 = red
9 = blue
8 = green
7 = yellow
6 = orange

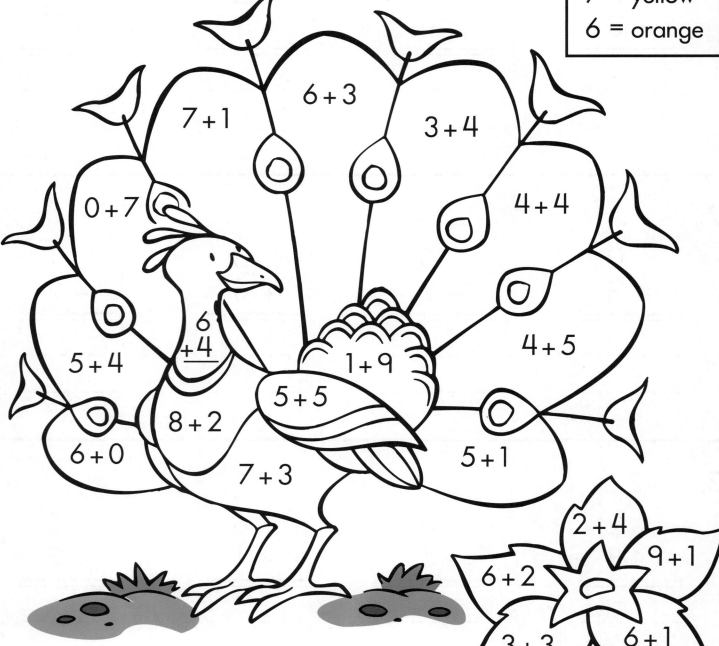

Addition Facts to 10

Name_____ Date_____

Add.

1.

$5 + 5 = $ _____ $3 + 3 = $ _____

2.

$8 + 1 = $ _____ $2 + 7 = $ _____

3.

$3 + 2 = $ _____ $3 + 0 = $ _____

4.

$6 + 3 = $ _____ $4 + 4 = $ _____

5.

$2 + 1 = $ _____ $6 + 4 = $ _____

6.

$5 + 2 = $ _____ $1 + 4 = $ _____

7.

$7 + 3 = $ _____ $6 + 0 = $ _____

Addition Facts to 10

Name_____ Date_____

Add.

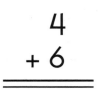

1.

```
    4        3        6        9        7
  + 6      + 3      + 2      + 1      + 0
 ======   ======   ======   ======   ======

 - - - -  - - - -  - - - -  - - - -  - - - -

 _____   _____   _____   _____   _____
```

2.

```
    8        2        3        4        1
  + 1      + 1      + 6      + 3      + 4
 ======   ======   ======   ======   ======

 - - - -  - - - -  - - - -  - - - -  - - - -

 _____   _____   _____   _____   _____
```

3.

```
    5        2        4        3        6
  + 5      + 3      + 4      + 1      + 2
 ======   ======   ======   ======   ======

 - - - -  - - - -  - - - -  - - - -  - - - -

 _____   _____   _____   _____   _____
```

4.

```
    2        3        6        4        4
  + 8      + 5      + 0      + 5      + 1
 ======   ======   ======   ======   ======

 - - - -  - - - -  - - - -  - - - -  - - - -

 _____   _____   _____   _____   _____
```

Turnaround Addition Facts

Name_____ Date_____

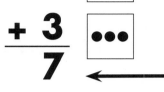

4
+ 3
7

The sum is the same.

3
+ 4
7

Write the sums. Then match.

1.
```
  5
+ 4
  9
```
```
  2
+ 6
```

5.
```
  3
+ 2
```
```
  2
+ 3
```

2.
```
  3
+ 7
```
```
  4
+ 5
  9
```

6.
```
  3
+ 6
```
```
  4
+ 6
```

3.
```
  6
+ 2
```
```
  7
+ 0
```

7.
```
  5
+ 2
```
```
  6
+ 3
```

4.
```
  0
+ 7
```
```
  7
+ 3
```

8.
```
  6
+ 4
```
```
  2
+ 5
```

Subtraction: Sets

Name_____ Date_____

Count how many are left. Write the number.

1.

How many are left? $10 - 5 =$ _____5_____

2.

How many are left? $10 - 6 =$ _____

3.

How many are left? $9 - 5 =$ _____

4.

How many are left? $8 - 6 =$ _____

5.

How many are left? $9 - 3 =$ _____

Subtraction: Sets

Name_____ Date_____

Cross out and subtract.

1.

$$\begin{array}{r} 9 \\ -\ 4 \\ \hline \end{array}$$

5

2.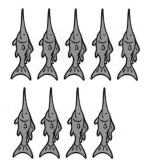

$$\begin{array}{r} 9 \\ -\ 8 \\ \hline \end{array}$$

_ _ _ _ _

How many are left? _____

3.

$$\begin{array}{r} 10 \\ -\ 8 \\ \hline \end{array}$$

_ _ _ _ _

How many are left? _____

4.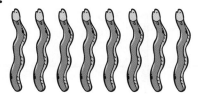

$$\begin{array}{r} 8 \\ -\ 5 \\ \hline \end{array}$$

_ _ _ _ _

How many are left? _____

5.

$$\begin{array}{r} 10 \\ -\ 7 \\ \hline \end{array}$$

_ _ _ _ _

How many are left? _____

6.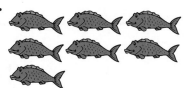

$$\begin{array}{r} 7 \\ -\ 2 \\ \hline \end{array}$$

_ _ _ _ _

How many are left? _____

7.

$$\begin{array}{r} 6 \\ -\ 3 \\ \hline \end{array}$$

_ _ _ _ _

How many are left? _____

Name_____ Date_____

Circle the correct number sentence.

1.

$9 - 3 = 6$

$10 - 3 = 7$

2.

$8 - 6 = 2$

$10 - 8 = 2$

3.

$9 - 6 = 3$

$10 - 6 = 4$

4.
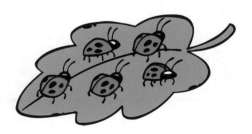

$7 - 5 = 2$

$10 - 5 = 5$

5.

$8 - 4 = 4$

$9 - 4 = 5$

Subtraction Facts to 10

Name_____ Date_____

Cross out and subtract.

1.
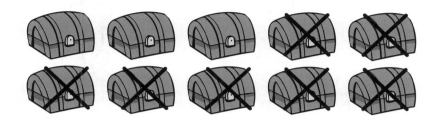

$$\begin{array}{r} 10 \\ -\ 7 \\ \hline \end{array}$$

3

2.

$$\begin{array}{r} 6 \\ -\ 1 \\ \hline \end{array}$$

3.
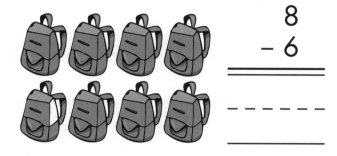

$$\begin{array}{r} 8 \\ -\ 6 \\ \hline \end{array}$$

4.
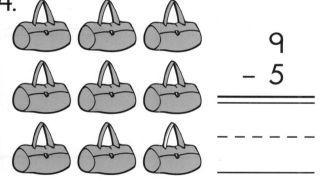

$$\begin{array}{r} 9 \\ -\ 5 \\ \hline \end{array}$$

5.

$$\begin{array}{r} 10 \\ -\ 4 \\ \hline \end{array}$$

6.
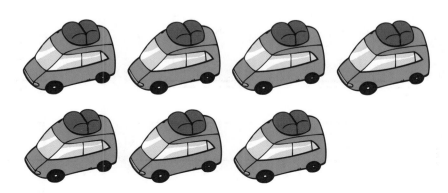

$$\begin{array}{r} 7 \\ -\ 6 \\ \hline \end{array}$$

Subtraction Facts to 10

Name_____ Date_____

Subtract.

1.

```
    6          8          4          9
  - 6        - 5        - 1        - 4
  ═════      ═════      ═════      ═════
  - - - -    - - - -    - - - -    - - - -
  _____      _____      _____      _____
```

2.

```
    5          7          9          3
  - 5        - 3        - 1        - 2
  ═════      ═════      ═════      ═════
  - - - -    - - - -    - - - -    - - - -
  _____      _____      _____      _____
```

3.

```
    8          2         10          7
  - 4        - 0        - 6        - 5
  ═════      ═════      ═════      ═════
  - - - -    - - - -    - - - -    - - - -
  _____      _____      _____      _____
```

Subtraction Facts to 10

Name_____ Date_____

Subtract.

1.

$$\begin{array}{r} 10 \\ -\ 7 \\ \hline \end{array}$$

$$\begin{array}{r} 9 \\ -\ 6 \\ \hline \end{array}$$

$$\begin{array}{r} 5 \\ -\ 5 \\ \hline \end{array}$$

$$\begin{array}{r} 4 \\ -\ 1 \\ \hline \end{array}$$

2.

$$\begin{array}{r} 8 \\ -\ 3 \\ \hline \end{array}$$

$$\begin{array}{r} 7 \\ -\ 4 \\ \hline \end{array}$$

$$\begin{array}{r} 10 \\ -\ 5 \\ \hline \end{array}$$

$$\begin{array}{r} 2 \\ -\ 1 \\ \hline \end{array}$$

3.

$$\begin{array}{r} 5 \\ -\ 2 \\ \hline \end{array}$$

$$\begin{array}{r} 9 \\ -\ 7 \\ \hline \end{array}$$

$$\begin{array}{r} 8 \\ -\ 5 \\ \hline \end{array}$$

$$\begin{array}{r} 6 \\ -\ 2 \\ \hline \end{array}$$

Subtraction Facts to 10

Name_____ Date_____

Subtract.

1.

10	8	9	7	2
− 7	− 6	− 5	− 3	− 0

2.

9	4	9	9	9
− 9	− 2	− 7	− 6	− 2

3.

3	8	8	6	7
− 3	− 8	− 6	− 3	− 4

4.

10	5	7	5	6
− 2	− 4	− 5	− 3	− 5

Checking Subtraction

Name_____ Date_____

Subtract. Then add to check.

1.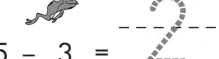

   5 – 3 = __2__ ✔   2 + 3 = __5__

2.

   9 – 5 = _____ ✔   4 + 5 = _____

3.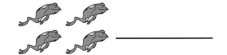

   6 – 4 = _____ ✔   2 + 4 = _____

4.

   10 – 3 = _____ ✔   7 + 3 = _____

5.

   9 – 6 = _____ ✔   3 + 6 = _____

147

Addition and Subtraction Practice

Name_____ Date_____

$4 + 3 =$ __7__

○ 5
○ 6
● 7

Solve. Then fill in the circle next to the correct answer.

1.

$3 + 1 =$ _____

○ 4
○ 5
○ 6

2.

$5 - 3 =$ _____

○ 4
○ 3
○ 2

3.

$10 - 9 =$ _____

○ 3
○ 2
○ 1

4.

$2 + 2 =$ _____

○ 2
○ 3
○ 4

5.

$8 - 4 =$ _____

○ 4
○ 3
○ 2

6.

$6 + 3 =$ _____

○ 9
○ 10
○ 11

7.

$7 + 2 =$ _____

○ 7
○ 8
○ 9

8.

$9 - 4 =$ _____

○ 6
○ 5
○ 4

Addition and Subtraction Practice

Name_____ Date_____

$$\begin{array}{r} 2 \\ +\ 7 \\ \hline 9 \end{array}$$

○ 8
● 9
○ 10

GREAT JOB!

Solve. Then fill in the circle next to the correct answer.

1.

$$\begin{array}{r} 7 \\ -\ 4 \\ \hline \end{array}$$

○ 4
○ 3
○ 2

2.

$$\begin{array}{r} 4 \\ +\ 5 \\ \hline \end{array}$$

○ 8
○ 9
○ 10

3.

$$\begin{array}{r} 5 \\ +\ 3 \\ \hline \end{array}$$

○ 6
○ 7
○ 8

4.

$$\begin{array}{r} 8 \\ -\ 7 \\ \hline \end{array}$$

○ 2
○ 1
○ 0

5.

$$\begin{array}{r} 10 \\ -\ 6 \\ \hline \end{array}$$

○ 6
○ 5
○ 4

6.

$$\begin{array}{r} 2 \\ +\ 1 \\ \hline \end{array}$$

○ 2
○ 3
○ 4

7.

$$\begin{array}{r} 3 \\ +\ 7 \\ \hline \end{array}$$

○ 10
○ 11
○ 12

8.

$$\begin{array}{r} 5 \\ -\ 5 \\ \hline \end{array}$$

○ 0
○ 5
○ 10

Addition Word Problems

Name_____ Date_____

Read each problem. Write the answer.

1. Rita sent 3 s.

Rob sent 6 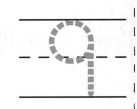s.

How many 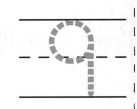s in all?

_____

_____

2. Kate bought 6 s.

Ken bought 2 s.

How many s in all?

_____

_____

_____

3. Liz has 4 s.

Len has 3 s.

How many s in all?

_____

_____

_____

4. Zack has 2 s.

Matt has 2 s.

How many s in all?

_____

_____

_____

Addition Word Problems

Name_____ Date_____

Read each problem. Write the answer.

1. Erin has 4 🐟.
   Mary has 2 🐟.

   How many 🐟 in all? _____

2. Bob has 2 🐸s.
   David has 3 🐸s.

   How many 🐸s in all? _____

3. Susie picked 7 🌼s.
   Jane picked 2 🌼s.

   How many 🌼s in all? _____

4. John has 5 🚗s.
   Ed has 3 🚗s.

   How many 🚗s in all? _____

5. Jenny has 3 🧸s.
   Joey has 1 🧸.

   How many 🧸s in all? _____

151

Subtraction Word Problems

Name_____ Date_____

Read each problem. Write the answer.

1. 4 🧸s on the 🛋️.
   3 🧸s fall off.

   How many 🧸s are left? _____

2. 8 👧s on the 🛋️.
   5 👧s fall off.

   How many 👧s are left? _____

3. 8 ⚾s on the 🛋️.
   3 ⚾s roll off.

   How many ⚾s are left? _____

4. 6 🚗s on the 🛋️.
   4 🚗s roll off.

   How many 🚗s are left? _____

5. 10 🔔s on the 🛋️.
   5 🔔s fall off.

   How many 🔔s are left? _____

Subtraction Word Problems

Name_____ Date_____

Read each problem. Write the answer.

1. 7 🐦 s.
   5 fly away.
   How many are left? $7 - 5 =$ _____

2. 5 🐭 .
   4 run away.
   How many are left? $5 - 4 =$ _____

3. 9 🕯 s.
   3 go out.
   How many are left? $9 - 3 =$ _____

4. 10 🌼 s.
   7 get picked.
   How many are left? $10 - 7 =$ _____

5. 8 🍪 s.
   4 are eaten.
   How many are left? $8 - 4 =$ _____

Addition and Subtraction Word Problems

Name_____ Date_____

Read each problem. Write the answer.

1. 4 🐞 s.
   2 more 🐞 s come.   How many 🐞 s in all? _____

2. 8 🐟.
   4 🐟 swim away.   How many 🐟 are left? _____

3. 3 🐱 s.
   3 more 🐱 s come.   How many 🐱 s in all? _____

4. 4 🐕 s.
   5 more 🐕 s come.   How many 🐕 s in all? _____

5. 6 🐷 s.
   2 🐷 s run away.   How many 🐷 s are left? _____

Name_____ Date_____

Match.

12
13
11
17
18
15

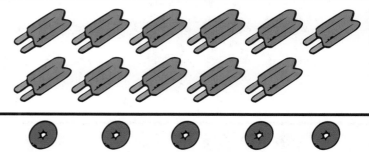
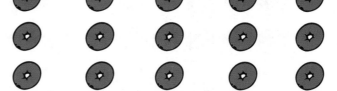
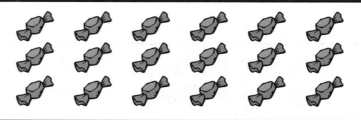
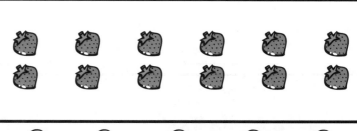
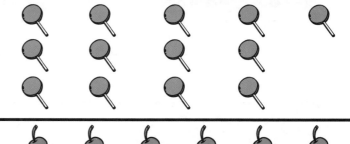

Addition: Sets

Name_____ Date_____

Count. Write how many.

1.

9 + 9 = in all

18

2

+ = in all

_ _ _ _ _ + _ _ _ _ _ = _ _ _ _ _

3.

+ = in all

_ _ _ _ _ + _ _ _ _ _ = _ _ _ _ _

4.

+ = in all

_ _ _ _ _ + _ _ _ _ _ = _ _ _ _ _

5.   in all

_ _ _ _ _ + _ _ _ _ _ = _ _ _ _ _

Addition: Sets

Name_____ Date_____

Write how many.

1.
```
   9
+  8
```
_7_ in all

2.
```
   8
+  7
```
_____ in all

3.
```
   8
+  9
```
_____ in all

4.
```
   9
+  7
```
_____ in all

5.
```
   6
+  9
```
_____ in all

6.
```
   6
+  7
```
_____ in all

7.
```
   7
+  7
```
_____ in all

Unit 2

Addition Facts to 18

Name_____ Date_____

Add to find the sums.

1.

9   +   9   =   18

2.

9 + 8 = _____   9 + 7 = _____

3.

3 + 8 = _____   9 + 3 = _____   8 + 5 = _____

4.

8 + 4 = _____   7 + 7 = _____   9 + 6 = _____

5.

8 + 8 = _____   9 + 2 = _____   5 + 7 = _____

6.

8 + 6 = _____   4 + 7 = _____   6 + 6 = _____

    158

Addition Facts to 18

Name_____ Date_____

$$\begin{array}{r} 10 \\ +\ 8 \\ \hline 18 \end{array}$$

Add to find the sums.

1.

$$\begin{array}{r} 9 \\ +8 \\ \hline \end{array} \qquad \begin{array}{r} 9 \\ +2 \\ \hline \end{array} \qquad \begin{array}{r} 9 \\ +9 \\ \hline \end{array} \qquad \begin{array}{r} 6 \\ +8 \\ \hline \end{array} \qquad \begin{array}{r} 7 \\ +5 \\ \hline \end{array}$$

2.

$$\begin{array}{r} 6 \\ +9 \\ \hline \end{array} \qquad \begin{array}{r} 7 \\ +6 \\ \hline \end{array} \qquad \begin{array}{r} 9 \\ +5 \\ \hline \end{array} \qquad \begin{array}{r} 8 \\ +8 \\ \hline \end{array} \qquad \begin{array}{r} 6 \\ +6 \\ \hline \end{array}$$

3.

$$\begin{array}{r} 3 \\ +8 \\ \hline \end{array} \qquad \begin{array}{r} 5 \\ +8 \\ \hline \end{array} \qquad \begin{array}{r} 7 \\ +4 \\ \hline \end{array} \qquad \begin{array}{r} 4 \\ +8 \\ \hline \end{array} \qquad \begin{array}{r} 7 \\ +7 \\ \hline \end{array}$$

Unit 2

159

Addition Practice

Name_____ Date_____

○○○○○○○ ○○○○

7 + 4 = 11

Write the missing number.

1.

$\begin{array}{r} 6 \\ + \\ \hline 14 \end{array}$
$\begin{array}{r} \\ + 9 \\ \hline 12 \end{array}$
$\begin{array}{r} 8 \\ + \\ \hline 13 \end{array}$
$\begin{array}{r} \\ + 9 \\ \hline 17 \end{array}$

2.

$\begin{array}{r} \\ + 8 \\ \hline 16 \end{array}$
$\begin{array}{r} \\ + 6 \\ \hline 15 \end{array}$
$\begin{array}{r} 9 \\ + \\ \hline 18 \end{array}$
$\begin{array}{r} 9 \\ + \\ \hline 13 \end{array}$

3.

$\begin{array}{r} 3 \\ + \\ \hline 11 \end{array}$
$\begin{array}{r} \\ + 7 \\ \hline 13 \end{array}$
$\begin{array}{r} 5 \\ + \\ \hline 15 \end{array}$
$\begin{array}{r} \\ + 7 \\ \hline 14 \end{array}$

Adding Three Numbers

Name _____ Date _____

Unit 2

Add.

1.

5	4	3	3	3
3	1	4	2	4
+ 6	+ 9	+ 8	+ 7	+ 5

2.

4	3	2	6	5
4	6	5	1	2
+ 9	+ 7	+ 3	+ 4	+ 6

Adding Three Numbers

Name_____ Date_____

Add.

1.
    6
    2
 + 1
_____

3
2
+ 5

5
3
+ 4

3
3
+ 3

6
1
+ 5

2.
    4
    1
 + 8

7
2
+ 5

2
4
+ 6

8
1
+ 2

5
1
+ 3

3.
    7
    1
 + 4

2
3
+ 6

3
6
+ 4

4
4
+ 4

5
2
+ 6

Subtraction: Sets

Name_____ Date_____

Subtract.

1.

$15 - 8 =$ _____ 7

2.

$14 - 9 =$ _____

3.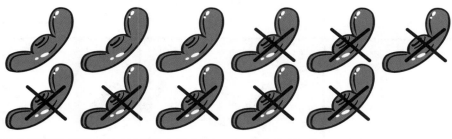

$11 - 8 =$ _____

4.

$18 - 9 =$ _____

5.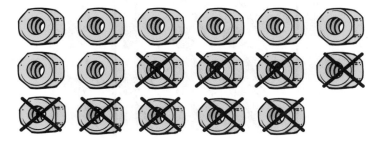

$17 - 9 =$ _____

163

Subtraction: Sets

Name_____ Date_____

Cross out and subtract.

1.

$$\begin{array}{r} 15 \\ -\ 7 \\ \hline \end{array}$$

8

2.

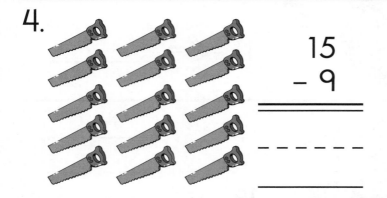

$$\begin{array}{r} 16 \\ -\ 8 \\ \hline \end{array}$$

3.

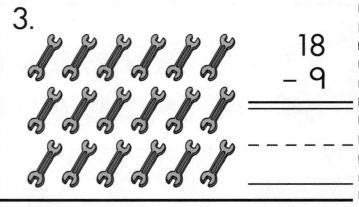

$$\begin{array}{r} 18 \\ -\ 9 \\ \hline \end{array}$$

4.

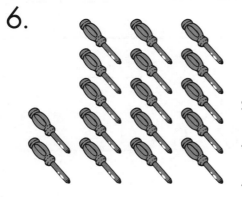

$$\begin{array}{r} 15 \\ -\ 9 \\ \hline \end{array}$$

5.

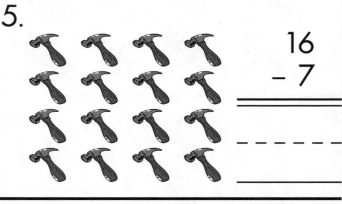

$$\begin{array}{r} 16 \\ -\ 7 \\ \hline \end{array}$$

6.

$$\begin{array}{r} 17 \\ -\ 8 \\ \hline \end{array}$$

7.

$$\begin{array}{r} 12 \\ -\ 7 \\ \hline \end{array}$$

Subtraction Facts to 18

Name_____ Date _____

Subtract.

1.

18	13	17	15
− 9	− 8	− 9	− 7

2.

14	15	16	11
− 8	− 9	− 8	− 2

3.

13	10	14	16
− 4	− 7	− 7	− 9

Subtraction Facts to 18

Name_____ Date_____

Subtract. Then match the problems with the same answers.

$10 - 7 =$ - - - - -

$15 - 9 =$ - - - - -

$15 - 8 =$ - - - - -

$16 - 8 =$ - - - - -

$12 - 6 =$ - - - -

$14 - 9 =$ - - - -

$10 - 5 =$ - - - - -

$14 - 7 =$ - - - - -

$17 - 9 =$ - - - - -

$13 - 9 =$ - - - - -

$11 - 7 =$ - - - -

$11 - 8 =$ - - - - -

Subtraction Facts to 18

Name_____ Date_____

Subtract. Then use the code to color the quilt.

2 = red	4 = yellow	6 = blue	8 = pink
3 = orange	5 = green	7 = purple	9 = brown

1.
$$11 - 9$$ $$17 - 8$$ $$13 - 7$$ $$11 - 4$$ $$14 - 5$$ $$13 - 8$$ $$18 - 9$$

2.
$$16 - 7$$ $$14 - 6$$ $$13 - 9$$ $$12 - 3$$ $$13 - 5$$ $$15 - 7$$

3.
 $$13 - 4$$ $$14 - 8$$ $$15 - 6$$ $$11 - 6$$

4.
$$11 - 2$$  $$11 - 3$$ $$12 - 5$$ $$11 - 7$$ $$12 - 9$$

5.
$$11 - 5$$ $$17 - 9$$ $$16 - 8$$ $$14 - 7$$ $$11 - 8$$

Subtraction Practice

Name_____ Date_____

Write the missing number.

1.

$$14 - \underline{} = 6$$

$$12 - \underline{} = 9$$

$$10 - 5 = 7$$

$$10 - \underline{} = 7$$

2.

$$\underline{} - 8 = 8$$

$$18 - \underline{} = 9$$

$$13 - \underline{} = 6$$

$$\underline{} - 4 = 8$$

3.

$$17 - \underline{} = 8$$

$$\underline{} - 7 = 4$$

$$14 - \underline{} = 9$$

$$9 - \underline{} = 5$$

4.

$$\underline{} - 6 = 3$$

$$10 - \underline{} = 8$$

$$14 - \underline{} = 7$$

$$\underline{} - 6 = 5$$

Checking Subtraction

Name_____ Date_____

Subtract. Then add to check.

1.

13 – 9 = $\underline{}$ - - - - - - - - - - - - $\underline{}$ + 9 = 13

2.

12 – 5 = $\underline{}$ - - - - - - - - - - - - $\underline{}$ + 5 = 12

3.

16 – 7 = $\underline{}$ - - - - - - - - - - - - $\underline{}$ + 7 = 16

4.

11 – 3 = $\underline{}$ - - - - - - - - - - - - $\underline{}$ + 3 = 11

5.

14 – 8 = $\underline{}$ - - - - - - - - - - - - $\underline{}$ + 8 = 14

6.

18 – 9 = $\underline{}$ - - - - - - ✔ - - - - - - $\underline{}$ + 9 = 18

Addition and Subtraction Review

Name_____ Date_____

Solve the problems. If the answer is correct, circle it.
If it is incorrect, change it to make it correct.

1.

$$
\begin{array}{r} 7 \\ + 6 \\ \hline 12 \end{array}
\qquad
\begin{array}{r} 15 \\ - 9 \\ \hline 6 \end{array}
\qquad
\begin{array}{r} 18 \\ - 9 \\ \hline 8 \end{array}
\qquad
\begin{array}{r} 8 \\ + 3 \\ \hline 11 \end{array}
$$

2.

$$
\begin{array}{r} 13 \\ - 4 \\ \hline 9 \end{array}
\qquad
\begin{array}{r} 6 \\ + 5 \\ \hline 11 \end{array}
\qquad
\begin{array}{r} 14 \\ - 7 \\ \hline 8 \end{array}
\qquad
\begin{array}{r} 16 \\ - 8 \\ \hline 9 \end{array}
$$

3.

$$
\begin{array}{r} 6 \\ + 8 \\ \hline 14 \end{array}
\qquad
\begin{array}{r} 9 \\ + 9 \\ \hline 17 \end{array}
\qquad
\begin{array}{r} 12 \\ - 5 \\ \hline 8 \end{array}
\qquad
\begin{array}{r} 17 \\ - 8 \\ \hline 9 \end{array}
$$

4.

$$
\begin{array}{r} 10 \\ - 3 \\ \hline 6 \end{array}
\qquad
\begin{array}{r} 14 \\ - 7 \\ \hline 7 \end{array}
\qquad
\begin{array}{r} 4 \\ + 7 \\ \hline 12 \end{array}
\qquad
\begin{array}{r} 7 \\ + 8 \\ \hline 16 \end{array}
$$

Name_____ Date_____

8 + 3 = 11

○ 10
● 11
○ 12

Solve. Then fill in the circle next to the correct answer.

1.

13 – 7 = _____

○ 8
○ 7
○ 6

2.

2 + 9 = _____

○ 9
○ 10
○ 11

3.

5 + 6 = _____

○ 11
○ 12
○ 13

4.

12 – 9 = _____

○ 5
○ 4
○ 3

5.

15 – 8 = _____

○ 8
○ 7
○ 6

6.

8 + 6 = _____

○ 12
○ 13
○ 14

7.

7 + 4 = _____

○ 10
○ 11
○ 12

8.

16 – 8 = _____

○ 9
○ 8
○ 7

Addition Word Problems

Name_____ Date_____

Read each problem. Write the answer.

1.

Kim has 5 🪙s.

She got 6 more 🪙s.

How many 🪙s does she have now?

$$\begin{array}{r} 5 \\ + 6 \\ \hline \end{array}$$

_ _ _ _ _

_____

2.

Rick found 8 🐚s.

Pam found 7 🐚s.

How many 🐚s did they find in all?

$$\begin{array}{r} 8 \\ + 7 \\ \hline \end{array}$$

_ _ _ _ _

_____

3.

Matt has 6 🚗s.

Rob has 9 🚗s.

How many 🚗s do they have in all?

$$\begin{array}{r} 6 \\ + 9 \\ \hline \end{array}$$

_ _ _ _ _

_____

4.

Pat has 7 🪀s.

Her mother gave her 4 more.

How many 🪀s does she have now?

$$\begin{array}{r} 7 \\ + 4 \\ \hline \end{array}$$

_ _ _ _ _

_____

Addition Word Problems

Name_____ Date_____

Read each problem. Write the answer.

1.

Ryan saw 7 s.

Then he saw 6 more s.

How many s did he see in all?

$$\begin{array}{r} 7 \\ +\ 6 \\ \hline \end{array}$$
- - - - - - -
_____

2.

Nick collected 8 s.

He found 3 more s.

How many s did he have in all?

$$\begin{array}{r} 8 \\ +\ 3 \\ \hline \end{array}$$
- - - - - - -
_____

3.

Ashley planted 9 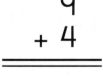s.

Frank planted 4 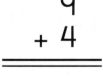s.

How many 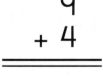s were planted in all?

$$\begin{array}{r} 9 \\ +\ 4 \\ \hline \end{array}$$
- - - - - - -
_____

4.

Kyle has 9 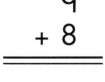s.

His dad gave him 8 more 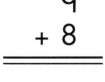s.

How many s does he have now?

$$\begin{array}{r} 9 \\ +\ 8 \\ \hline \end{array}$$
- - - - - - -
_____

Subtraction Word Problems

Name_____ Date_____

Read each problem. Write the answer.

1.

I had 11 ⬤s.

5 ⬤s popped.

How many ⬤s are left?

$$\begin{array}{r} 11 \\ -\ 5 \\ \hline \end{array}$$

_ _ _ _ _ _

_____

2.

I saw 13 🦆s.

4 🦆s swam away.

How many 🦆s are left?

$$\begin{array}{r} 13 \\ -\ 4 \\ \hline \end{array}$$

_ _ _ _ _ _

_____

3.

I have 9 🪙s.

I need 16 🪙s.

How many more 🪙s do I need?

$$\begin{array}{r} 16 \\ -\ 9 \\ \hline \end{array}$$

_ _ _ _ _ _

_____

4.

I had 16 🪐s.

I gave away 8 🪐s.

How many 🪐s do I have left?

$$\begin{array}{r} 16 \\ -\ 8 \\ \hline \end{array}$$

_ _ _ _ _ _

_____

Subtraction Word Problems

Name_____ Date_____

Read each problem. Write the answer.

1.

John had 17 s.

He gave 8 s to Ray.

How many s does John have left?

```
  17
-  8
=====

- - - - -

_____
```

2.

Mary had 16 s.

She broke 7 s.

How many s does she have left?

```
  16
-  7
=====

- - - - -

_____
```

3.

There were 12 🐰s.

4 🐰s hopped away.

How many 🐰s are left?

```
  12
-  4
=====

- - - - -

_____
```

4.

Mrs. Gray's class had 15 s.

They ate 9 🧁s.

How many s are left?

```
  15
-  9
=====

- - - - -

_____
```

Name_____ Date_____

Read each problem. Write a number sentence and solve.

1. Farmer Dan had 13 corn plants in the field. He harvested 6 of them. How many corn plants are left in the field?

$$13$$
$$- 6$$
$$\overline{7}$$

_____

2. Tara bought 9 petunias and 7 pansies. How many flowers did she buy altogether?

_____

3. Marci picked 15 flowers from the garden. She put 8 flowers in a vase and gave the rest away. How many flowers did Marci give away?

_____

4. Keisha picked 12 tomatoes from the garden. She used 5 tomatoes for a sauce and saved the rest for a salad. How many tomatoes did Keisha save?

_____

5. Evan planted 5 green pepper plants and 9 red pepper plants. How many pepper plants did he plant altogether?

_____

6. Carlos picked 3 red apples and 9 green apples. How many apples did he pick altogether?

_____

Two-Dimensional Shapes

Name_____ Date_____

square   circle   triangle   rectangle

Match.

Two-Dimensional Shapes

Name_____ Date_____

Trace each shape.

square   circle   triangle   rectangle

Write **S** on all the squares.
Write **T** on all the triangles.

Write **C** on all the circles.
Write **R** on all the rectangles.

Three-Dimensional Shapes

Name_____ Date_____

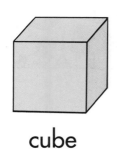   

cube　　　　　cylinder　　　　cone　　　　sphere

Match.

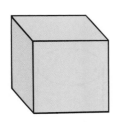

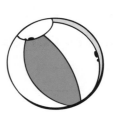

Three-Dimensional Shapes

Name_____ Date_____

Trace each shape.

cube   cylinder   cone   sphere

Color the **cubes** yellow.
Color the **cones** blue.

Color the **cylinders** green.
Color the **spheres** orange.

Congruent Shapes

Name_____ Date_____

Congruent shapes are the same shape and size.

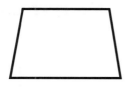 

same size

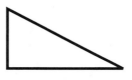

 same shape

Color the shapes that are **congruent**.

1.

2.

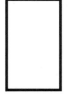 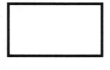

3.

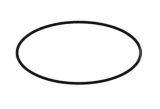  

4.

Unit 3

Shape and Pattern Practice

Name_____ Date_____

1. Color the **circle**.

2. Color the **rectangle**.

3. Draw what comes next. Color a pattern.

4. Color the shapes that are **congruent**.

5. Color the **cube**.

6. Color the **cone**.

Bar Graphs

Name_____ Date_____

Count each shape on page 178.
Color the graph to show how many
of each shape you counted.

Unit 3

10				
9				
8				
7				
6				
5				
4				
3				
2				
1				

☐ ◯ △ ▭

Bar Graphs

Name_____ Date_____

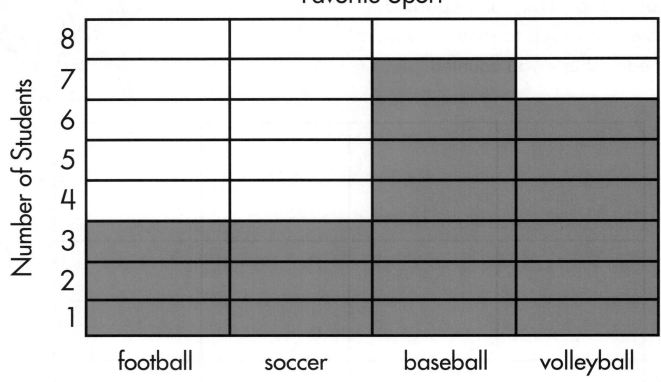

Favorite Sport

Use the graph to answer the questions.

1. How many students play football? — — — — — — — — — —

2. How many students play baseball? — — — — — — — — — —

3. How many students play soccer? — — — — — — — — — —

4. How many students play volleyball? — — — — — — — — — —

Picture Graphs

Name_____ Date_____

Favorite Ice Cream

vanilla	
chocolate	
strawberry	
chocolate chip	

Use the graph to answer the questions.

1. How many students like chocolate ice cream? _____

2. How many students like vanilla ice cream? _____

3. How many students like chocolate chip ice cream? _____

4. How many students like strawberry ice cream? _____

Graph Practice

Name_____ Date_____

Use the graphs to answer the questions.

Dinner Time

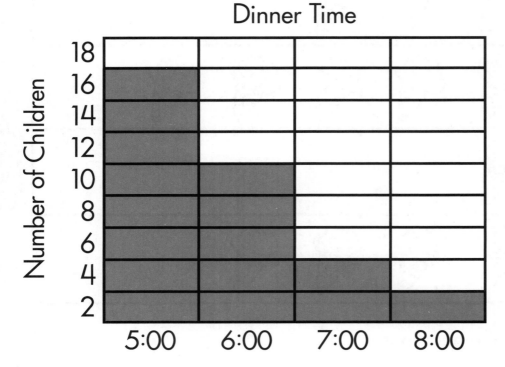

How many said...

_____

1. 7:00? - - - - - -
_____

2. 6:00? - - - - - -
_____

3. 8:00? - - - - - -
_____

4. 5:00? - - - - - -
_____

Favorite Pizza

pepperoni	🍕🍕🍕🍕🍕
cheese	🍕🍕🍕🍕
mushroom	🍕
sausage	🍕🍕🍕

🍕 = 1 child

How many said...

_____

5. pepperoni? - - - - - -
_____

6. sausage? - - - - - -
_____

7. mushroom? - - - - - -
_____

8. cheese? - - - - - -
_____

One Half

Name_____ Date_____

$$\frac{1\ \text{part shaded}}{2\ \text{equal parts}}$$

$\frac{1}{2}$ or one half is shaded.

Two equal parts are halves.

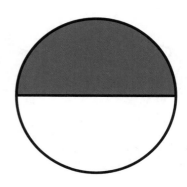

Circle the shapes that show halves. Color $\frac{1}{2}$ of each shape.

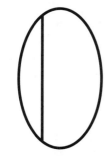
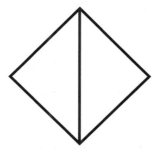
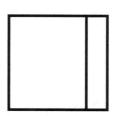

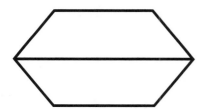
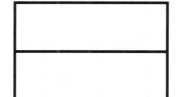
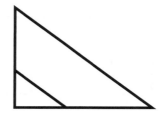

One Fourth

Name_____ Date_____

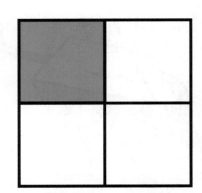

$\dfrac{1 \text{ part shaded}}{4 \text{ equal parts}}$

$\frac{1}{4}$ or one fourth is shaded.

Four equal parts are fourths.

Circle the shapes that show fourths. Color $\frac{1}{4}$ of each shape.

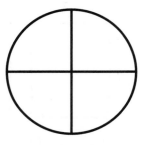 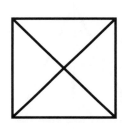 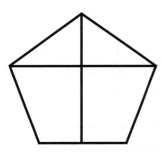

  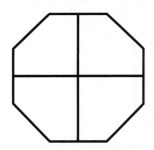

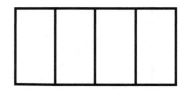 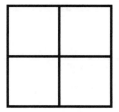 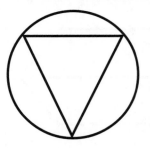

One Third

Name_____ Date_____

$\dfrac{1 \text{ part shaded}}{3 \text{ equal parts}}$

$\dfrac{1}{3}$ or one third is shaded.

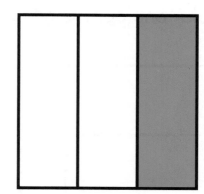

Three equal parts are thirds.

Circle the shapes that show thirds. Color $\dfrac{1}{3}$ of each shape.

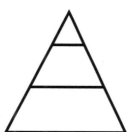

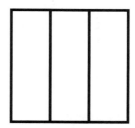

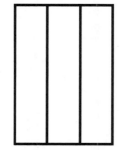

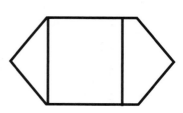

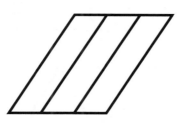

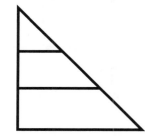

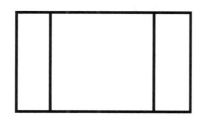

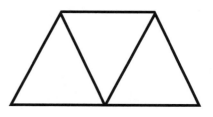

Fraction Practice

Name_____ Date_____

Color one part. Circle the fraction that names the colored part.

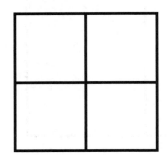

$\frac{1}{2}$ $\frac{1}{3}$ $\frac{1}{4}$

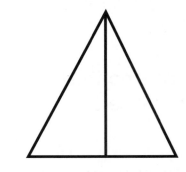

$\frac{1}{2}$ $\frac{1}{3}$ $\frac{1}{4}$

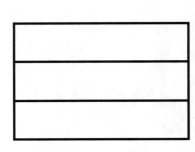

$\frac{1}{2}$ $\frac{1}{3}$ $\frac{1}{4}$

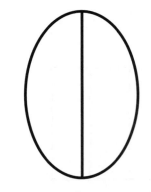

$\frac{1}{2}$ $\frac{1}{3}$ $\frac{1}{4}$

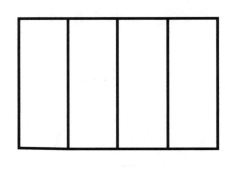

$\frac{1}{2}$ $\frac{1}{3}$ $\frac{1}{4}$

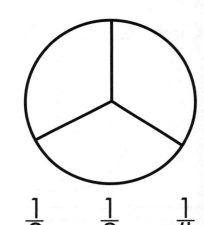

$\frac{1}{2}$ $\frac{1}{3}$ $\frac{1}{4}$

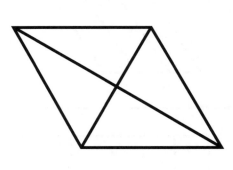

$\frac{1}{2}$ $\frac{1}{3}$ $\frac{1}{4}$

$\frac{1}{2}$ $\frac{1}{3}$ $\frac{1}{4}$

$\frac{1}{2}$ $\frac{1}{3}$ $\frac{1}{4}$

Tens and Ones

Name_____ Date_____

= | tens | ones |
|---|---|
| **5** | **6** |

56

Count the tens and ones. Write the number.

1.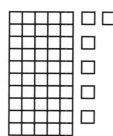

tens	ones

_____ tens _____ ones = _____

2.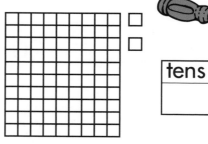

tens	ones

_____ tens _____ ones = _____

3.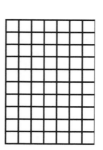

tens	ones

_____ tens _____ ones = _____

4.

tens	ones

_____ tens _____ ones = _____

5.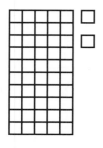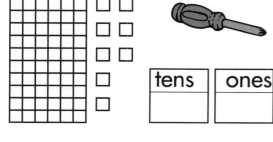

tens	ones

_____ tens _____ ones = _____

6.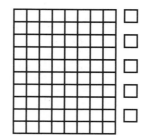

tens	ones

_____ tens _____ ones = _____

Numbers: Expanded Form

Name_____ Date_____

Write the number.

1. 30 + 5 = _35_   80 + 2 = _____   70 + 1 = _____

2. 60 + 3 = _____   40 + 7 = _____   20 + 2 = _____

3. 10 + 9 = _____   90 + 1 = _____   50 + 6 = _____

4. 30 + 2 = _____   80 + 5 = _____   60 + 8 = _____

Write an addition sentence.

5. 49 = ___ + ___   26 = ___ + ___   15 = ___ + ___

6. 53 = ___ + ___   45 = ___ + ___   62 = ___ + ___

7. 74 = ___ + ___   80 = ___ + ___   79 = ___ + ___

8. 57 = ___ + ___   61 = ___ + ___   98 = ___ + ___

Place Value Practice

Name_____ Date_____

Match.

8 tens and 3 ones	97	50 + 8
5 tens and 8 ones	58	30 + 1
3 tens and 1 one	31	90 + 7
9 tens and 7 ones	26	80 + 9
8 tens and 9 ones	64	60 + 4
7 tens and 5 ones	83	20 + 6
6 tens and 4 ones	75	40 + 3
2 tens and 6 ones	89	10 + 7
1 ten and 7 ones	43	80 + 3
4 tens and 3 ones	17	70 + 5

Unit 4

Place Value Practice

Name_____ Date_____

Count how many tens and ones. Write the number.

1.       ____ ____ = _____
    tens   ones

2.    (3 grapes images)   ____ ____ = _____
    tens   ones

3.       ____ ____ = _____
    tens   ones

Write how many tens and ones.

4. 35 = _____ tens _____ ones   54 = _____ tens _____ones

5. 81 = _____ tens _____ ones   29 = _____ tens _____ones

Write the number.

6. 4 tens and 3 ones = _____   1 ten and 6 ones = _____

7. 6 tens and 0 ones = _____   9 tens and 9 ones = _____

Adding Ones and Tens

Name_____ Date_____

tens	ones
3	0
+ 2	0
5	0

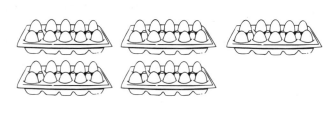

First add the ones. Then add then tens.

1.

tens	ones
4	0
+ 1	0
5	0

tens	ones
7	0
+ 2	0

2.

30	10	40	50	60	50
+ 30	+ 70	+ 30	+ 20	+ 30	+ 40

3.

60	50	80	40	10	40
+ 20	+ 30	+ 10	+ 20	+ 40	+ 40

Unit 4

Adding Ones and Tens

Name_____ Date_____

Add. Then find the balloon with the same sum and color it.

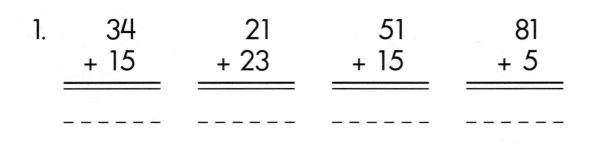

1.
34	21	51	81
+ 15	+ 23	+ 15	+ 5

2.
60	43	70	21
+ 29	+ 15	+ 7	+ 44

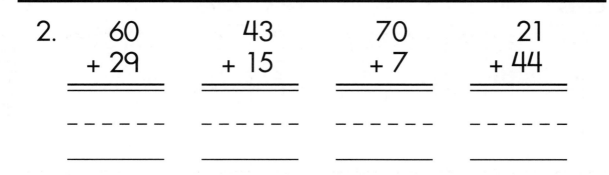

3.
27	32	42	21
+ 12	+ 23	+ 50	+ 72

4.
53	62	43	91
+ 26	+ 16	+ 44	+ 7

Balloons: 49, 44, 92, 86, 79, 93, 89, 58, 65, 78, 39, 55, 66, 98, 87, 77

Adding Ones and Tens

Name_____ Date_____

Add.

Don't forget! Add the ones first.

1.
   26
+ 43
═══════

   31
+ 42
═══════

   20
+ 34
═══════

   30
+ 9
═══════

2.
   41
+ 57
═══════

   52
+ 32
═══════

   64
+ 11
═══════

   52
+ 7
═══════

3.
   26
+ 43
═══════

   31
+ 42
═══════

   20
+ 34
═══════

   30
+ 18
═══════

4.
   22
+ 17
═══════

   30
+ 28
═══════

   33
+ 14
═══════

   24
+ 13
═══════

Adding Three Numbers

Name_____ Date_____

Add.

1.   24   17
         10   61
     + 15   + 10

"Remember to add the ones and then the tens."

2.   11   21   10   12   23
      13   30   35   21   32
   + 43   + 32   + 34   + 15   + 13

3.   13   31   64   27   30
      62   41   20   12   12
   + 24   + 20   + 13   + 50   + 54

4.   20   50   27   40   75
      30   12   12   31   11
   + 41   + 13   + 50   + 14   + 12

Adding Three Numbers

Name_____ Date_____

Add.

1.
$$\begin{array}{r} 26 \\ 11 \\ +\ 52 \\ \hline \end{array}$$
$$\begin{array}{r} 33 \\ 40 \\ +\ 15 \\ \hline \end{array}$$
$$\begin{array}{r} 36 \\ 10 \\ +\ 22 \\ \hline \end{array}$$
$$\begin{array}{r} 13 \\ 31 \\ +\ 30 \\ \hline \end{array}$$
$$\begin{array}{r} 52 \\ 26 \\ +\ 10 \\ \hline \end{array}$$

2.
$$\begin{array}{r} 14 \\ 51 \\ +\ 24 \\ \hline \end{array}$$
$$\begin{array}{r} 41 \\ 21 \\ +\ 11 \\ \hline \end{array}$$
$$\begin{array}{r} 70 \\ 15 \\ +\ 13 \\ \hline \end{array}$$
$$\begin{array}{r} 16 \\ 20 \\ +\ 30 \\ \hline \end{array}$$
$$\begin{array}{r} 10 \\ 30 \\ +\ 25 \\ \hline \end{array}$$

3.
$$\begin{array}{r} 22 \\ 33 \\ +\ 44 \\ \hline \end{array}$$
$$\begin{array}{r} 10 \\ 11 \\ +\ 12 \\ \hline \end{array}$$
$$\begin{array}{r} 27 \\ 12 \\ +\ 40 \\ \hline \end{array}$$
$$\begin{array}{r} 37 \\ 31 \\ +\ 21 \\ \hline \end{array}$$
$$\begin{array}{r} 15 \\ 14 \\ +\ 60 \\ \hline \end{array}$$

4.
$$\begin{array}{r} 70 \\ 15 \\ +\ 12 \\ \hline \end{array}$$
$$\begin{array}{r} 50 \\ 12 \\ +\ 24 \\ \hline \end{array}$$
$$\begin{array}{r} 44 \\ 23 \\ +\ 32 \\ \hline \end{array}$$
$$\begin{array}{r} 16 \\ 31 \\ +\ 52 \\ \hline \end{array}$$
$$\begin{array}{r} 61 \\ 16 \\ +\ 11 \\ \hline \end{array}$$

Unit 4

Subtracting Ones and Tens

Name_____ Date_____

tens	ones
3	8
− 2	3
1	5

First subtract the ones. Then subtract the tens.

1.

tens	ones
5	6
− 2	5

tens	ones
4	7
− 1	4

4.

39	65	98	73	84
− 28	− 21	− 40	− 43	− 72

4.

95	67	82	24	96
− 62	− 44	− 51	− 12	− 32

Subtracting Ones and Tens

Name_____ Date_____

Subtract.

Don't forget!
Subtract the ones.
Then subtract
the tens.

1.
```
   48          97          99          87
 - 24        - 62        - 73
```
= 81

_ _ _ _ _   _ _ _ _ _   _ _ _ _ _   _ _ _ _ _
_____   _____   _____   _____

2.
```
   97          45          68          43
 - 33        - 14        - 45        - 12
```

_ _ _ _ _   _ _ _ _ _   _ _ _ _ _   _ _ _ _ _
_____   _____   _____   _____

3.
```
   67          66          79          98
 - 35        - 24        - 42        - 56
```

_ _ _ _ _   _ _ _ _ _   _ _ _ _ _   _ _ _ _ _
_____   _____   _____   _____

4.
```
   39          27          55          79
 - 13        - 16                    - 22
```
= 31

_ _ _ _ _   _ _ _ _ _   _ _ _ _ _   _ _ _ _ _
_____   _____   _____   _____

Subtracting Ones and Tens

Name_____ Date_____

Subtract.

1. $\begin{array}{r}64\\-23\\\hline\end{array}$ $\begin{array}{r}16\\-6\\\hline\end{array}$ $\begin{array}{r}32\\-11\\\hline\end{array}$ $\begin{array}{r}45\\-13\\\hline\end{array}$ $\begin{array}{r}64\\-23\\\hline\end{array}$

2. $\begin{array}{r}81\\-70\\\hline\end{array}$ $\begin{array}{r}93\\-61\\\hline\end{array}$ $\begin{array}{r}78\\-56\\\hline\end{array}$ $\begin{array}{r}49\\-27\\\hline\end{array}$ $\begin{array}{r}59\\-18\\\hline\end{array}$

3. $\begin{array}{r}36\\-3\\\hline\end{array}$ $\begin{array}{r}68\\-34\\\hline\end{array}$ $\begin{array}{r}95\\-14\\\hline\end{array}$ $\begin{array}{r}87\\-43\\\hline\end{array}$ $\begin{array}{r}74\\-63\\\hline\end{array}$

4. $\begin{array}{r}98\\-33\\\hline\end{array}$ $\begin{array}{r}58\\-30\\\hline\end{array}$ $\begin{array}{r}47\\-21\\\hline\end{array}$ $\begin{array}{r}60\\-40\\\hline\end{array}$ $\begin{array}{r}89\\-52\\\hline\end{array}$

Name_____ Date_____

$$\begin{array}{r} 11 \\ + \ 3 \\ \hline 14 \end{array}$$

○ 12
○ 13
● 14

Solve. Then fill in the circle next to the correct answer.

1.
$$\begin{array}{r} 23 \\ + \ 1 \\ \hline \end{array}$$
○ 23
○ 24
○ 25

2.
$$\begin{array}{r} 89 \\ - \ 43 \\ \hline \end{array}$$
○ 47
○ 46
○ 45

3.
$$\begin{array}{r} 65 \\ + \ 2 \\ \hline \end{array}$$
○ 60
○ 66
○ 67

4.
$$\begin{array}{r} 23 \\ + \ 41 \\ \hline \end{array}$$
○ 22
○ 46
○ 64

5.
$$\begin{array}{r} 54 \\ - \ 3 \\ \hline \end{array}$$
○ 52
○ 51
○ 50

6.
$$\begin{array}{r} 32 \\ - \ 11 \\ \hline \end{array}$$
○ 22
○ 21
○ 20

7.
$$\begin{array}{r} 60 \\ + \ 10 \\ \hline \end{array}$$
○ 7
○ 60
○ 70

8.
$$\begin{array}{r} 45 \\ - \ 22 \\ \hline \end{array}$$
○ 13
○ 23
○ 22

Unit 4

Addition and Subtraction Practice

Name_____ Date_____

$$\begin{array}{r} 40 \\ -\ 20 \\ \hline 20 \end{array}$$

○ 30
● 20
○ 10

Solve. Then fill in the circle next to the correct answer.

1.
$$\begin{array}{r} 60 \\ -\ 20 \\ \hline \end{array}$$
○ 60
○ 50
○ 40

2.
$$\begin{array}{r} 40 \\ +\ 30 \\ \hline \end{array}$$
○ 71
○ 70
○ 80

3.
$$\begin{array}{r} 37 \\ -\ 5 \\ \hline \end{array}$$
○ 32
○ 31
○ 30

4.
$$\begin{array}{r} 64 \\ +\ 14 \\ \hline \end{array}$$
○ 77
○ 68
○ 78

5.
$$\begin{array}{r} 34 \\ +\ 24 \\ \hline \end{array}$$
○ 38
○ 58
○ 54

6.
$$\begin{array}{r} 82 \\ +\ 16 \\ \hline \end{array}$$
○ 98
○ 99
○ 88

7.
$$\begin{array}{r} 78 \\ -\ 53 \\ \hline \end{array}$$
○ 26
○ 25
○ 24

8.
$$\begin{array}{r} 55 \\ +\ 21 \\ \hline \end{array}$$
○ 65
○ 76
○ 56

Addition and Subtraction Practice

Name_____ Date_____

Solve. Then fill in the circle next to the correct answer.

1.

$$\begin{array}{r} 25 \\ + 14 \\ \hline \end{array}$$

- ○ 49
- ○ 39
- ○ 31

2.

$$\begin{array}{r} 84 \\ - 61 \\ \hline \end{array}$$

- ○ 23
- ○ 24
- ○ 25

3.

$$\begin{array}{r} 73 \\ - 20 \\ \hline \end{array}$$

- ○ 90
- ○ 93
- ○ 53

4.

$$\begin{array}{r} 56 \\ + 23 \\ \hline \end{array}$$

- ○ 73
- ○ 79
- ○ 33

5.

$$\begin{array}{r} 66 \\ - 33 \\ \hline \end{array}$$

- ○ 33
- ○ 99
- ○ 22

6.

$$\begin{array}{r} 32 \\ + 46 \\ \hline \end{array}$$

- ○ 77
- ○ 79
- ○ 78

7.

$$\begin{array}{r} 48 \\ + 20 \\ \hline \end{array}$$

- ○ 28
- ○ 68
- ○ 78

8.

$$\begin{array}{r} 97 \\ - 11 \\ \hline \end{array}$$

- ○ 86
- ○ 88
- ○ 90

9.

$$\begin{array}{r} 26 \\ - 13 \\ \hline \end{array}$$

- ○ 12
- ○ 13
- ○ 18

10.

$$\begin{array}{r} 37 \\ + 32 \\ \hline \end{array}$$

- ○ 99
- ○ 74
- ○ 69

Unit 4

Addition Word Problems

Name_____ Date_____

Read each problem.
Write a number sentence and solve.

STICKER SHOP

WAY TO GO!

1. One day, Mr. Perez sold 32 puffy animal stickers and 57 plain animal stickers. How many animal stickers did he sell that day?

_____

2. Mr. Perez ordered 52 new shiny stickers and 26 new puffy stickers. How many new stickers did Mr. Perez order?

SUPER

_____

3. Ms. Ross bought 87 car stickers and 12 happy face stickers. How many stickers did Ms. Ross buy?

_____

4. Julie's scout troop bought 31 puffy stickers and 48 shiny stickers. How many stickers did the troop buy?

_____

5. Mrs. Patel bought 24 "Good Work" stickers and 51 star stickers. How many stickers did Mrs. Patel buy?

WAY TO GO!

_____

6. The Sticker Club bought 37 elephant stickers and 21 bear stickers. How many stickers did the club buy?

_____

Addition Word Problems

Name_____ Date_____

Read each problem.
Write a number sentence and solve.

1. Manuel bought a truck and markers. How many tokens did he spend?

_____

2. Hunter bought two coloring books. How many tokens did he spend?

_____

3. Kameisha bought a doll and stickers. How many tokens did she spend?

_____

4. Nick bought stickers and a sticker book. How many tokens did he spend?

_____

5. Liz bought a coloring book and markers. How many tokens did she spend?

_____

6. Mai bought a stuffed bear and a coloring book. How many tokens did she spend?

_____

7. Who spent the most tokens?

_____

8. Who spent the fewest tokens?

_____

Subtraction Word Problems

Name_____ Date_____

Read each problem.
Write a number sentence and solve.

1. There are 38 boys and 49 girls at the Stars game. How many more girls than boys are at the game?

_____

2. There are 74 children and 96 adults at the Stars game. How many more adults than children are at the game?

_____

3. Manny sells 42 sodas and 67 bottled waters. How many more bottled waters than sodas are sold?

_____

4. Jane sells 45 bags of peanuts and 95 hot dogs. How many more hot dogs than peanuts are sold?

_____

5. The Stars sell 56 pennants. Of those, 14 are small pennants and the rest are large pennants. How many large pennants are sold?

_____

6. The Stars play 65 games at home out of a total of 99 games. How many games are played away from home?

_____

Subtraction Word Problems

Name_____   Date_____

Read each problem.
Write a number sentence and solve.

1. Of a total of 62 children at the fair, 30 are girls. How many boys are at the fair?

_____

2. There are 62 children and 41 adults at the fair. How many more children than adults are at the fair?

_____

3. Mr. Brown prepares 27 hamburgers, but he only sells 15 of them. How many hamburgers are not sold?

_____

4. Of 89 families that buy raffle tickets, only 47 of them win prizes. How many families do not win prizes?

_____

5. Amy sells 78 bags of popcorn. Of those, 36 are regular-size bags, and the rest are super-size. How many super-size bags of popcorn are sold?

_____

6. Mr. Chen had 38 school sweatshirts, but he sold 15 of them. How many school sweatshirts did Mr. Chen have left?

_____

Name_____ Date_____

Read each problem.
Write a number sentence and solve.

1. There were 85 students who went to the zoo. Only 42 of them were girls. How many boys went to the zoo?

_____

2. Cathy took 24 pictures while at the zoo. Her teacher took 41 pictures. How many pictures did they take altogether?

_____

3. George counted 24 monkeys playing on the high wire. Then 13 more came out of their cave. How many monkeys were there altogether?

_____

4. There were 39 birds spotted in the tree. After someone yelled, only 10 were left. How many birds flew away?

_____

5. The elephants had 55 visitors on Monday and 32 visitors on Tuesday. How many visitors did they have altogether?

_____

6. Mary bought 41 peanuts to feed the animals. She used 20 to feed the elephants. How many peanuts did she have left?

_____

Counting to 100

Name_____ Date_____

Write the numbers to finish the chart.

1	2			5			8		10
11		13				17		19	20
21			24	25				29	30
31		33			36		38	39	
	42		44			47			50
51				55	56				60
61			64			67		69	
71		73			76				80
	82			85			88		90
91			94		96			99	100

Unit 5

211

Odd and Even Numbers

Name_____ Date_____

Odd numbers end in **1**, **3**, **5**, **7**, or **9**.
Even numbers end in **0**, **2**, **4**, **6**, or **8**.

Circle the **odd** numbers.

1. 12   17   43   96   25   34   51   60

2. 27   28   6   15   67   50   4   88

3. 11   9   6   24   30   22   23   91

4. 44   47   5   19   10   13   20   86

Circle the **even** numbers.

5. 75   80   93   52   46   33   73   90

6. 18   29   31   66   7   40   82   89

7. 2   21   49   53   50   78   81   35

8. 55   64   58   3   71   65   70   83

Count how many you circled for each. Write the number.

9. _____ odd numbers   10. _____ even numbers

Number Order: Before

Name_____ Date_____

25   **26**   **27**   28

26 comes **before 27**.

Circle the number that comes **before**.

1. I am before 37. What number am I? **(36)** **38** **47**	2. I am before 89. What number am I? **90** **98** **88**
3. I am before 17. What number am I? **16** **18** **37**	4. I am before 23. What number am I? **25** **24** **22**
5. I am before 50. What number am I? **60** **49** **51**	6. I am before 61. What number am I? **67** **64** **60**
7. I am before 98. What number am I? **100** **99** **97**	8. I am before 80. What number am I? **81** **79** **90**

Unit 5

Number Order: After

Name_____ Date _____

56   **57**   **58**   59

58 comes **after 57**.

Write the number that comes **after**.

1. 9 |10| 12 |___| 19 |___|

2. 23 |___| 28 |___| 30 |___|

3. 36 |___| 40 |___| 44 |___|

4. 49 |___| 54 |___| 61 |___|

5. 66 |___| 70 |___| 78 |___|

6. 87 |___| 92 |___| 99 |___|

Number Order: Between

33   **34**   35

34 comes **between 33** and **35**.

Write the number that comes **between**.

1. 26 _27_ 28

2. 51 _____ 53

3. 83 _____ 85

4. 32 _____ 34

5. 74 _____ 76

14 _____ 16

68 _____ 70

40 _____ 42

95 _____ 97

29 _____ 31

Unit 5

Number Order: Least to Greatest

Name_____ Date_____

45   54   60

The numbers from **least** to **greatest** are **45**, **54**, **60**.

Write each group of numbers from **least** to **greatest**.

1. 10   30   20

    10   20   30

3. 18   23   14

    ___   ___   ___

5. 48   52   45

    ___   ___   ___

7. 34   41   29

    ___   ___   ___

2. 75   57   68

    ___   ___   ___

4. 35   27   31

    ___   ___   ___

6. 67   82   53

    ___   ___   ___

8. 60   47   59   9. 90   68   77

    ___   ___   ___   ___   ___   ___

Inequality Symbols

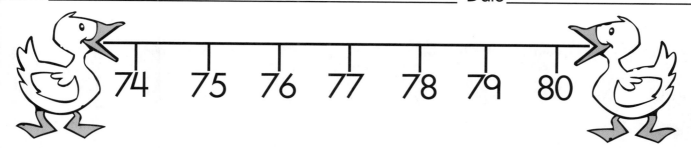

< means "is **less than**"   > means "is **greater than**"
76 < 78   77 > 75

Write **<** or **>** to complete each sentence.
Be sure the duck's mouth is open to the **greatest** number.

1. | 10 _>_ 9 | | 36 ___ 40 | | 18 ___ 81 |

2. | 80 ___ 68 | | 54 ___ 40 | | 16 ___ 71 |

3. | 36 ___ 39 | | 25 ___ 29 | | 50 ___ 49 |

4. | 27 ___ 72 | | 82 ___ 85 | | 71 ___ 79 |

5. | 60 ___ 59 | | 30 ___ 39 | | 48 ___ 50 |

6. | 39 ___ 31 | | 56 ___ 85 | | 19 ___ 21 |

Unit 5

Ordinal Numbers

Name_____ Date_____

first **1st** second **2nd** third **3rd** fourth **4th** fifth **5th** sixth **6th** seventh **7th** eighth **8th** ninth **9th** tenth **10th**

Color the toy to show the ordinal number.

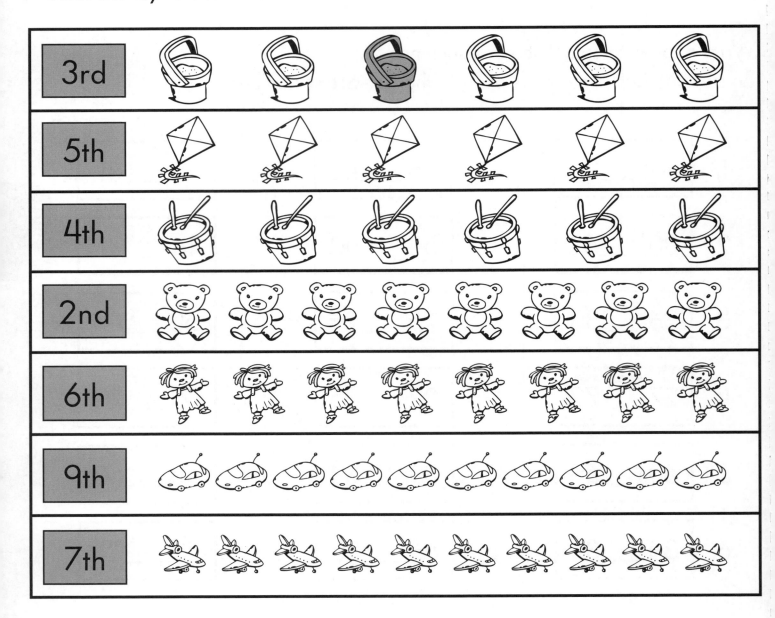

Number Order Practice

Name_____ Date_____

Write the missing numbers.

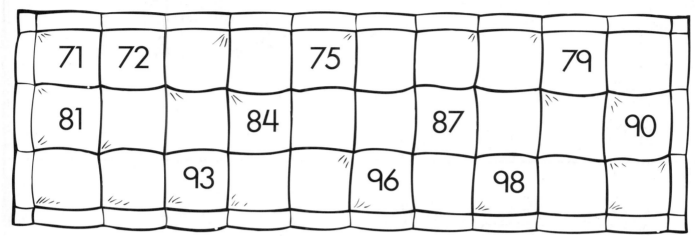

71	72			75				79	
81			84			87			90
		93			96		98		

Write the missing numbers.

1. 53 ____   ____ 20   36 ____ 38   49 ____

2. ____ 31   87 ____   12 ____ 14   ____ 75

Write **<** or **>** to complete each sentence.

3. | 79 ____ 80 | | 65 ____ 56 | | 41 ____ 38 | | 27 ____ 72 |

4. | 32 ____ 23 | | 87 ____ 90 | | 80 ____ 70 | | 55 ____ 52 |

Solve the riddles. Write the numbers.

5. I am an odd number between 40 and 50. You say me when you count by 5's. What number am I?

6. I am an even number greater than 89 and less than 93. You say me when you count by 10's. What number am I?

Skip Counting: By 10's

Name_____ Date_____

Count by 10's. Write the number.

10, 20, 30

1. _____ _ _ _ _ _ _____

2. _____ _ _ _ _ _ _____

3. _____ _ _ _ _ _ _____

4. _____ _ _ _ _ _ _____

5. _____ _ _ _ _ _ _____

Skip Counting: By 5's

Name_____ Date_____

Count by 5's. Write the missing numbers.

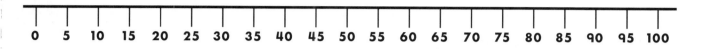

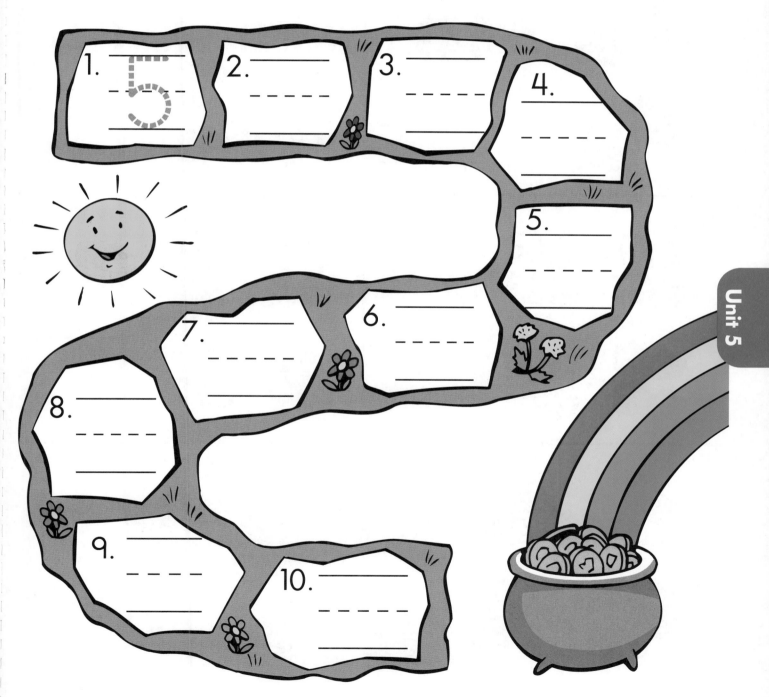

Unit 5

Skip Counting: By 2's

Name_____ Date_____

Count by 2's. Write the number.

1.

_____

- - - - - - - - - - -

_____

2.

_____

- - - - - - - - - - -

_____

3.

_____

- - - - - - - - - - -

_____

4.

_____

- - - - - - - - - - -

_____

5.

_____

- - - - - - - - - - -

_____

Skip Counting Practice

Name_____ Date_____

Count by 2's. Write the missing numbers.

1.  2  4  6  ___  ___

2.  ___  ___  ___  ___  20

Count by 5's. Write the missing numbers.

3.  5  10  ___  ___  ___

4.  ___  ___  40  ___  50

Count by 10's. Write the missing numbers.

5.  10  20  ___ 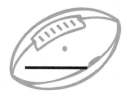 ___  ___

6.  ___  70  ___  ___ 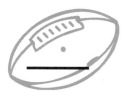 ___

Unit 5

Number Patterns

Name_____ Date_____

Look for the number patterns. Circle them.

Count by 1's from 57 to 62.   Count by 1's from 22 to 27.
Count by 2's from 2 to 12.   Count by 5's from 70 to 95.
Count by 2's from 88 to 100.   Count by 10's from 10 to 50.
Count by 5's from 15 to 45.   Count by 10's from 60 to 100.

100	98	96	94	92	90	88	85
45	0	22	23	24	25	26	27
23	14	95	90	85	80	75	70
30	19	12	60	70	80	90	100
25	57	58	59	60	61	62	80
30	10	20	30	40	50	43	85
15	20	25	30	35	40	45	67
10	91	2	4	6	8	10	12

Money: Pennies

Name_____ Date _____

Draw lines to match the pennies with the amounts. A penny is worth 1¢.

1¢

2¢

3¢

4¢

5¢

6¢

7¢

8¢

Money: Nickels

Name_____ Date_____

Count by 5's. Write the amount.

A NICKEL IS WORTH 5¢.

1. 15 ¢

2. _____ ¢

3. _____ ¢

4. _____ ¢

5. _____ ¢

6. _____ ¢

Money: Nickels and Pennies

Name_____ Date_____

Count the money in each bank. Write the amount.

1.

¢
_____

2.

¢
_____

3.

¢
_____

4.

¢
_____

5.

¢
_____

6.

¢
_____

Unit 5

Money: Dimes

Name_____ Date_____

Count by 10's. Write the amount.

A dime is worth 10 cents.

1.

40 ¢
_____

2.

_____ ¢

3.

_____ ¢

4.

_____ ¢

5.

_____ ¢

6.

_____ ¢

Money: Dimes and Pennies

Name_____ Date_____

Count the money in each treasure chest. Write the amount.

1.

_____ ¢

2.

_____ ¢

3.

_____ ¢

4.
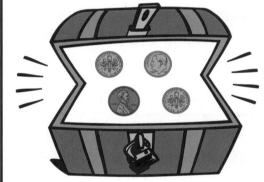

_____ ¢

5.

_____ ¢

6.

_____ ¢

Money Word Problems

Name_____ Date _____

Read each story problem. Write the answer.

1. Rebecca has two pennies in one hand.
   She has three dimes in the other hand.
   How much money does she have in all?

   ¢
   _____

2. Kyle has one nickel.
   He finds two more nickels.
   How much money does he have in all?

   ¢
   _____

3. Todd has one nickel.
   Bob has nine pennies.
   How much money do they have altogether?

   ¢
   _____

4. Jill has three dimes.
   Paul has five pennies.
   Who has more money?

   ¢
   _____

Money Practice

Name_____ Date_____

Count the money. Write the amount.

1.
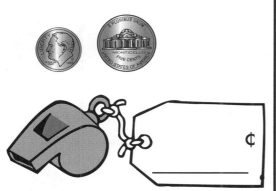

¢
_____

2.
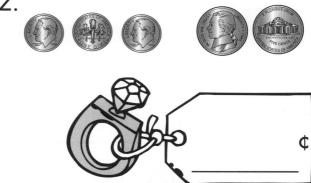

¢
_____

3.

¢
_____

4.

¢
_____

5.

¢
_____

6.
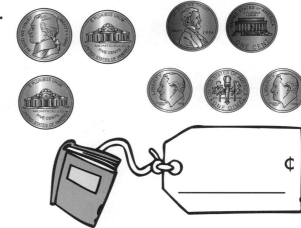

¢
_____

Unit 5

Money Practice

○ 31¢
● 36¢
○ 39¢

Count the money. Then fill in the circle next to the correct answer.

1.	2.
○ 20¢ ○ 25¢ ○ 29¢	○ 32¢ ○ 36¢ ○ 52¢
3. ○ 46¢ ○ 56¢ ○ 58¢	**4.** ○ 35¢ ○ 50¢ ○ 75¢
5. ○ 80¢ ○ 85¢ ○ 90¢	**6.** ○ 75¢ ○ 77¢ ○ 79¢
7. ○ 28¢ ○ 38¢ ○ 39¢	**8.** ○ 89¢ ○ 95¢ ○ 99¢

Time to the Hour

Name_____ Date_____

The **minute hand** is on **12**.
The **hour hand** is on **3**.
It is **3:00** or **3 o'clock**.

Circle the correct time.

1.

(5:00)   7:00   12:00   1:00   11:00   12:00

2.

8:00   10:00   11:00   9:00   1:00   2:00

3.

6 o'clock   3 o'clock   6 o'clock
7 o'clock   2 o'clock   12 o'clock

Unit 6

233

Time to the Hour

Name_____ Date_____

Draw a line from each clock to the matching time.

   5 o'clock

                                3 o'clock

                                1 o'clock

                                6 o'clock

                                8 o'clock

                                2 o'clock

                                9 o'clock

   4 o'clock

Name_____ Date_____

Write the time.

1.

_____ o'clock   _____ o'clock   _____ o'clock

2.

_____ o'clock   _____ o'clock   _____ o'clock

3.     (middle)   (right)

_____ o'clock   _____ o'clock   _____ o'clock

4.     (middle)   (right)

_____ o'clock   _____ o'clock   _____ o'clock

Unit 6

Time to the Hour

Name_____ Date_____

Write the time.

1.

9:00 _____   _____ : _____   _____ : _____

2.

_____ : _____   _____ : _____   _____ : _____

3.

_____ : _____   _____ : _____   _____ : _____

4.

_____ : _____   _____ : _____   _____ : _____

Time to the Hour

Name_____ Date_____

Draw the hour hand on each clock to show the time.

1.

3:00

12:00

6:00

2.

7:00

2:00

5:00

3.

11:00

8:00

1:00

4.

4:00

9:00

10:00

Unit 6

Time to the Half Hour

Name_____ Date _____

8:30 or **eight-thirty**

Circle the correct time.

1.

8:30   9:30

1:30   11:30

12:30   1:30

2.

7:30   8:30

5:30   6:30

2:30   3:30

3.

three-thirty

two-thirty

nine-thirty

eight-thirty

four-thirty

five-thirty

Time to the Half Hour

Name_____ Date_____

Draw a line from each clock to the matching time.

8:30

6:30

nine-thirty

7:30

5:30

 12:30

4:30

one-thirty

Unit 6

Time to the Half Hour

Name_____ Date_____

Write the time.

1.

<u>one</u>-thirty

_____-thirty

_____-thirty

2.

_____-thirty

_____-thirty

_____-thirty

3.

_____-thirty

_____-thirty

_____-thirty

4.

_____-thirty

_____-thirty

_____-thirty

Time to the Half Hour

Name_____ Date_____

Write the time.

1.

10:30

 :

 :

2.

 :

 :

 :

3.

 :

 :

 :

4.

 :

 :

 :

Name_____ Date_____

Draw the hour hand on each clock to show the time.

1.

   6:30   8:30   7:30

2.

   11:30   1:30   3:30

3.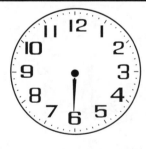

   9:30   10:30   12:30

4.

   5:30   2:30   4:30

Elapsed Time

Name_____ Date_____

Now it is **2 o'clock**.   One hour later it will be **3 o'clock**.

Draw clock hands to show the time one hour later. Write the time.

NOW   **LATER**

1.    12 o'clock   ____ o'clock

2.   4 o'clock   ____ o'clock

3.    7 o'clock   ____ o'clock

4.    10 o'clock   ____ o'clock

Unit 6

Time Word Problems

Name_____ Date_____

Read each problem. Write the answer.

1. Eric left home at 11 o'clock. It took 1 hour to get to the beach. What time did Eric get to the beach?

_____

2. Kate goes to camp at 8 o'clock. Pat goes to camp at 9 o'clock. Who goes to camp first?

_____

3. Samir got to the park at 3 o'clock. He went home at 5 o'clock. How long was Samir at the park?

_____

4. The soccer game starts at 6 o'clock. It ends one hour later. What time does the soccer game end?

_____

5. Meg left home at 9 o'clock. It took her 2 hours to get to Aunt Lin's. What time did Meg get to Aunt Lin's?

_____

6. Ben went to the pool at 2:00. He stayed for 1 hour. What time did Ben go home?

_____

Time Practice

Name_____ Date_____

Write the time.

1.

: _____

_____

: _____

2.

: _____

: _____

: _____

3.

: _____

: _____

: _____

4.

: _____

: _____

: _____

Time Practice

Name_____ Date_____

Circle the time.

ten-thirty   4 o'clock   6:00
eleven-thirty   2 o'clock   12:00

Draw lines to match the clocks with the same time.

11:00

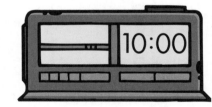
10:00

5:30

8:30

Time Practice

Name_____ Date_____

○ 7:00
● 8:00
○ 9:00

Fill in the circle next to the correct time.

1.  ○ 7:30 ○ 8:30 ○ 9:30	2.  ○ 7:00 ○ 8:00 ○ 9:00
3.  ○ 2:00 ○ 3:00 ○ 3:30	4.  ○ 4:30 ○ 5:00 ○ 5:30
5.  ○ 11:30 ○ 12:30 ○ 1:30	6.  ○ 5:00 ○ 6:00 ○ 12:30
7.  ○ 1:00 ○ 9:00 ○ 10:00	8. ○ 1:30 ○ 2:30 ○ 3:30

Unit 6

Reading a Calendar

Name_____ Date_____

Use the calendar to answer the questions.

1. What is the first day of the week? _____

2. How many days are in one week? _____

3. How many Mondays are in this month? _____

4. What day of the week is July 10? _____

5. What is the date of the picnic? _____

6. When is David's birthday? _____

7. When are the library books due? _____

8. When is the baseball game? _____

Months of the Year

Name_____ Date_____

Read each clue. Write the answer.

| January | February | March | April | May | June | July |
| August | September | October | November | December |

1. First month of the year   _____January_____

2. Last month of the year   _____

3. Month after June   _____

4. Month before September   _____

5. Month between May and July   _____

6. Second month of the year   _____

7. Tenth month of the year   _____

8. Third month of the year   _____

9. Month between March and May   _____

10. Fifth month of the year   _____

11. Month before October   _____

12. Month before December   _____

Unit 6

Measurement: Length in Inches

Name_____ Date_____

Write the number of inches.

1.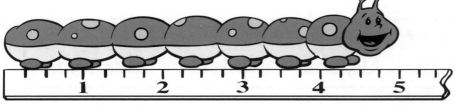

_**5**_ inch(es) long

2.

_____ inch(es) long

3.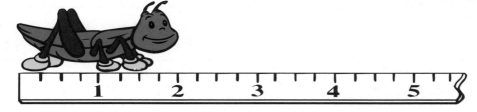

_____ inch(es) long

4.

_____ inch(es) long

5.

_____ inch(es) long

Measurement: Length in Inches

Name _____ Date _____

Write the number of inches.

1.

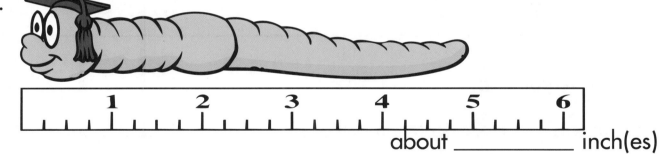

about _____ inch(es)

2.

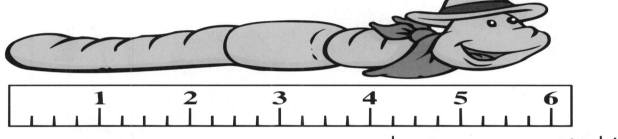

about _____ inch(es)

3.

about _____ inch(es)

4.

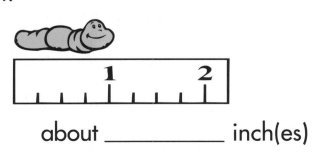

about _____ inch(es)

5.

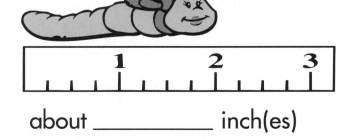

about _____ inch(es)

Measurement: Length in Inches

Name_____ Date_____

Use an inch ruler to measure each path on the map.
Write the number of inches.

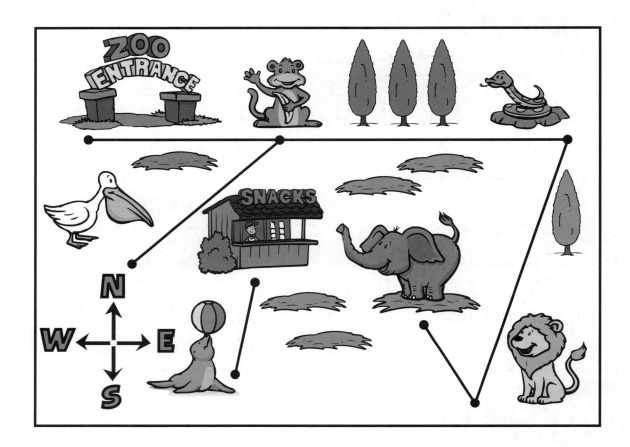

How long is the path:

1. From the Entrance to the monkeys? _____ inch(es)

2. From the Entrance to the snakes? _____ inch(es)

3. From the monkeys to the birds? _____ inch(es)

4. From the Snack Bar to the seals? _____ inch(es)

5. From the elephants to the lions? _____ inch(es)

6. From the lions to the snakes? _____ inch(es)

Measurement: Length in Centimeters

Name_____ Date_____

Write the number of centimeters.

1.
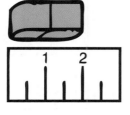

about _____ centimeters

2.
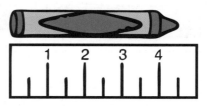

about _____ centimeters

3.
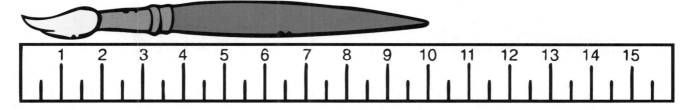

about _____ centimeters

4.
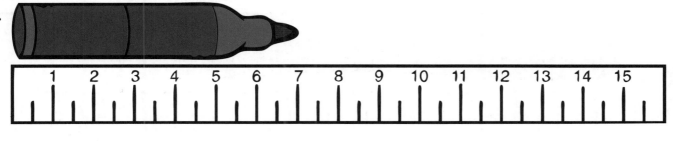

about _____ centimeters

5.
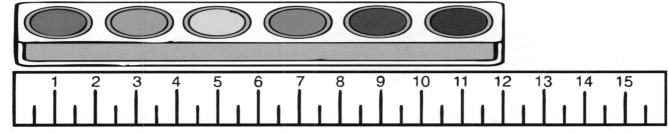

about _____ centimeters

Unit 6

Measurement: Length in Centimeters

Name_____ Date_____

Write the number of centimeters.

1.
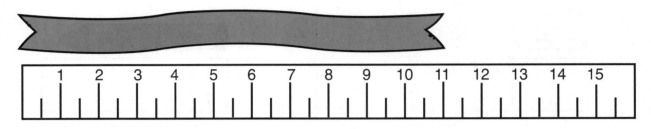

| 1 | 2 | 3 | 4 | 5 | 6 | 7 | 8 | 9 | 10 | 11 | 12 | 13 | 14 | 15 |

_____ centimeters

2.
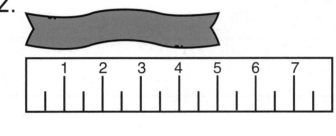

| 1 | 2 | 3 | 4 | 5 | 6 | 7 |

_____ centimeters

3.
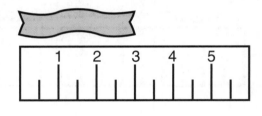

| 1 | 2 | 3 | 4 | 5 |

_____ centimeters

4.
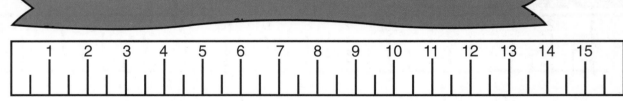

| 1 | 2 | 3 | 4 | 5 | 6 | 7 | 8 | 9 | 10 | 11 | 12 | 13 | 14 | 15 |

_____ centimeters

5.
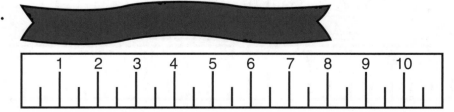

| 1 | 2 | 3 | 4 | 5 | 6 | 7 | 8 | 9 | 10 |

_____ centimeters

Name_____ Date_____

Write the number of centimeters.

1.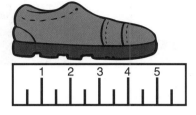

_____ centimeters

2.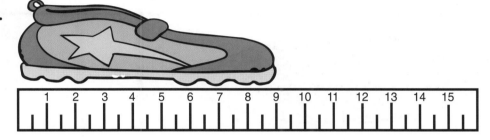

_____ centimeters

3.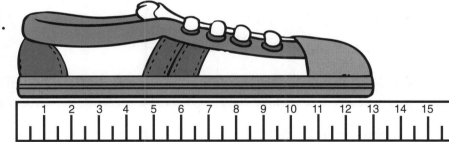

_____ centimeters

4.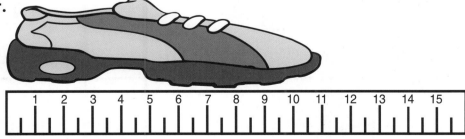

_____ centimeters

Measurement: Inches and Centimeters

Name_____ Date_____

Estimate the length of each fish.
Then use a ruler to measure the number of inches or centimeters.

1.

Estimate: _____ centimeters   Measure: _____ centimeters

2.

Estimate: _____ inches   Measure: _____ inches

3.

Estimate: _____ centimeters   Measure: _____ centimeters

4.

Estimate: _____ inches   Measure: _____ inches

5.

Estimate: _____ inches   Measure: _____ inches